Holt German

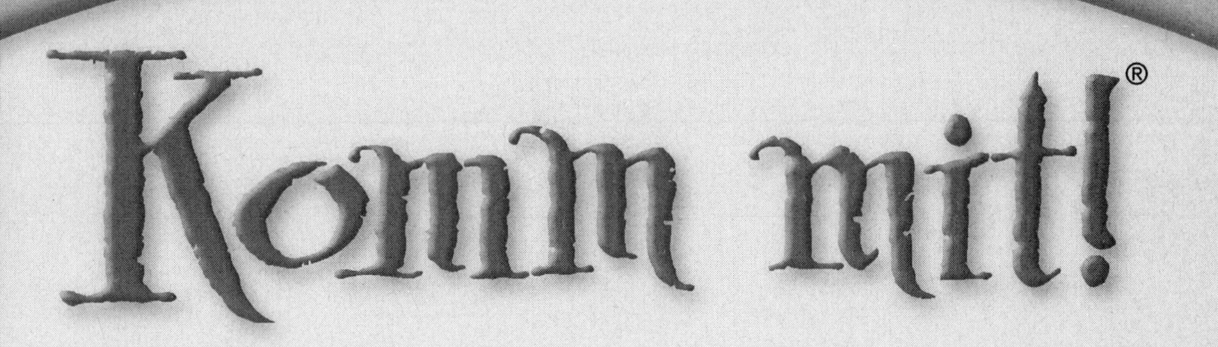

Grammar Tutor for Students of German

Levels 1, 2, and 3

HOLT, RINEHART AND WINSTON
A Harcourt Education Company
Austin • Orlando • Chicago • New York • Toronto • London • San Diego

Prepared by

George Winkler

Cover Photography Credits
(t) © Dana White/PhotoEdit/Picture Quest; (b) Digital Imagery® © 2003 PhotoDisc, Inc.

Printed in the United States of America

ISBN 0-03-065867-5

5 6 7 095 05 04

Table of Contents

To the Teacher vi
Grammar at a Glance vii

German 1

Kapitel 1
- Questions 1
- Nouns 3
- Definite Articles 5
- Subjects 7
- Subject Pronouns and the Verb *to be* 9

Kapitel 2
- Subjects and Verbs 11
- Conjugation of Verbs 13
- Subject-Verb Agreement 15
- Person and Number 17
- Present Tense 19
- Word Order: Position of the Verb in a Statement 21

Kapitel 3
- Modal Verbs: The **möchte**-forms 23
- Third-Person Pronouns 25

Kapitel 4
- Nouns and Their Plural Forms 27

Kapitel 5
- Direct Objects 29
- Subject and Direct Object (Noun Phrases) 31
- Direct Object Pronouns 33
- Separable-Prefix Verbs 35

Kapitel 6
- Word Order: Expressions of Time and Place 37

Kapitel 7
- Separable-Prefix Verbs and Modals 39
- Object Pronouns: Second Person 41

Kapitel 8
- Command Forms: The **du**-Command and the **ihr**-Command 43
- Sentences and Clauses 45

Kapitel 9
- Formal **Sie**-Command 47
- There is, there are 49
- Negation: **nicht** and **kein** 51

Kapitel 11
- Indirect Objects 53

Kapitel 12
- To know (Summary) 55
- Mood and Modal Verbs (Summary) 56
- Modal Verbs (Summary) 57

Answer Key: German 1 161

Table of Contents *continued*

German 2

Kapitel 1 (Wiederholung)
Verbs, Present Tense (Review) 61

Kapitel 2 (Wiederholung)
Modal Verbs (Review)........63
Meanings of Modal Verbs (Review) 65
Subjects, Direct and Indirect Objects (Review) 67

Kapitel 3
Past Tense 69
Past Participles................71
Present Perfect................73
Use of the Present Perfect Tense 75
Prepositions: Direction vs. Location..................77
Indirect Object Pronouns ...79

Kapitel 4
Reflexive Pronouns...........81
Reflexive Verbs.................83

Kapitel 5
Possessive Adjectives........85

Kapitel 6
Inclusive Command 87
Direct Objects in the Dative Case 89
Reflexive Verbs.................91
Dative Case instead of **für** + Accusative............93

Kapitel 7
Comparison 95
Adjectives........................97
Adjective Endings Following **ein**-Words 99

Kapitel 8
Adjective Endings Following **der** and **dieser**-Words 101

Kapitel 9
Prepositions...................103
Dative Prepositions 105
Accusative Prepositions...107

Kapitel 10
Prepositions Used with Verbs and Adjectives.....109
Noun Objects of a Preposition: **da**-Compounds and **wo**-Compounds.......111
Future Tense..................113

Kapitel 11
Polite Requests (**würde**-Forms)........................115
Unpreceded Adjectives 117
Polite Requests (**hätte**-Forms)........................119

Answer Key: German 2 175

Table of Contents continued

German 3

Kapitel 1 (Wiederholung)
The Conversational Past (Review) 123

Kapitel 2 (Wiederholung)
Adjectives (Review) 125

Kapitel 3
Infinitive Phrases 127

Kapitel 4
Ordinal Numbers 129
Relative Pronouns and Relative Clauses 131
Conditional Sentences 135
The Possessive: Genitive Case 137

Kapitel 5
Modal Verbs: Past Tense 139

Kapitel 6
Narrative Past (Imperfect) 141
Superlative Forms of Adjectives 143

Kapitel 7
Relative Clauses (continued) 145

Kapitel 8
Conjunctions 147

Kapitel 9
Subjunctive Forms of Modals 149
The Passive Voice 151
Conditional Sentences (continued) 153

Kapitel 10
Passive Voice (Summary) 155

Kapitel 11
Future Perfect and Perfect Infinitive 157

Answer Key: German 3 191

To the Teacher

Many students do not have a clear understanding of their own language and cannot, therefore, build on that understanding as they learn a second language. The intention of this *Grammar Tutor* is to explain the basic grammar concepts introduced and practiced in *Komm mit!* first in English, with English examples and activities, and then in German, so that students can relate the concept to something they do every day in English and thereby gain insights about how the grammar works before they attempt to learn it in the context of an entirely new language.

The *Grammar Tutor* presents in sequential order the main grammar points introduced in *Komm mit!,* Levels 1, 2, and 3. These grammar points are compared to English as appropriate, so that students can readily see the many similarities between the two languages. In some cases, they will, of course, see differences; however, as they compare and contrast the structures of German and English, they will no doubt accomplish one goal: they will increase their understanding of language in general and become better able to use it to communicate.

The explanation of each grammar concept is accompanied by examples, and each presentation is followed by an activity that allows students to verify that they have understood the explanation of the grammar concept. The concepts are presented first in English and then in German; the activity following the presentation has the same format in both languages, to enable students to quickly see the comparison between the two languages.

Following the initial activity is an activity that asks students to apply what they understood from the presentation. The final activity on each Activity Master encourages students to think about both the target language and their own.

On the following pages is a glossary of the grammar terms that are covered in this book. This "Grammar at a Glance" can serve as a quick reference to the more detailed material covered in the body of the *Grammar Tutor*.

Grammar at a Glance

accusative case (See **case.**)

adjective An adjective modifies a noun or a pronoun. (See also **demonstrative adjective, interrogative adjective,** and **possessive adjective.**)

EXAMPLES The Browns live in a **beautiful old** house.
Die Browns wohnen in einem **schönen alten** Haus.

adjective agreement (See **agreement.**)

adverb An adverb modifies a verb, an adjective, or another adverb.

EXAMPLES He eats **slowly,** but walks **briskly.**
Er isst **langsam,** aber er geht **schnell.**
She is a **well-**educated girl.
Sie ist ein **gut** erzogenes Mädchen.

agreement Agreement is the correspondence, or match, between grammatical forms. Grammatical forms agree when they have the same number or gender.

subject-verb agreement Subject-verb agreement refers to the form of a verb that goes with its subject.

EXAMPLES **I read** the paper in the morning, but **she reads** it in the evening.
Ich lese die Zeitung morgens, aber **sie liest** sie abends.

adjective agreement Adjective agreement refers to the form of an adjective that matches the number and gender of the noun it modifies.

EXAMPLES I like this **blue** sweater, and I would like a **brown** belt.
Mir gefällt dieser **blaue** Pulli, und ich möchte einen **braunen** Gürtel.

article An article refers to a noun. Articles are the most frequently used type of adjectives. The the three articles in English are *a, an,* and *the.*

definite article *The* is the definite article and refers to a specific noun.

EXAMPLES **The** dog won't come out of **the** house.
Der Hund kommt nicht aus **dem** Haus.

indefinite article *A* and *an* are the indefinite articles and refer to nonspecific nouns.

EXAMPLES They ate **an** apple and **a** pear.
Sie haben **einen** Apfel und **eine** Birne gegessen.

case Case refers to the function of a noun or pronoun in a sentence. In English, function is most often indicated by word order or context; in German, function is indicated by inflection (changes to the word) or by context.

EXAMPLES **My grandpa** lives in Bavaria. **Mein Opa** wohnt in Bayern.
I visit **my grandpa** in Bavaria. Ich besuche **meinen Opa** in Bayern.
I'll send **my grandpa** an e-mail. Ich schicke **meinem Opa** eine E-Mail.
This present is for **my grandpa.** Das Geschenk ist für **meinen Opa.**

accusative case Accusative case refers to a noun or pronoun that is functioning as either the direct object of a sentence, or the object of certain prepositions.

EXAMPLES **Whom** are you calling? Are you calling **your German friend** for **me**?
Wen rufst du an? Rufst du **deinen deutschen Freund** für **mich** an?

dative case Dative case refers to a noun or pronoun that is functioning as the indirect object of a sentence, the object of certain prepositions, or the direct object of certain special verbs.

EXAMPLES **To whom** are you giving the book? I'm giving **my father** the book.
Wem gibst du das Buch? Ich gebe **meinem Vater** das Buch.
I help **my brother** with **his homework**.
Ich helfe **meinem Bruder** mit **seinen Hausaufgaben**.

genitive case Genitive case refers to a noun or pronoun that is functioning as a possessor, the object of certain prepositions, or the object of certain special verbs.

EXAMPLES My sister's car is in front of the house.
Das Auto **meiner Schwester** steht vor dem Haus.
We are thinking **of the victims**. –We'll drive **despite** the weather.
Wir gedenken **der Opfer**.–Wir fahren **trotz** des schlecht**en** Wetters.

nominative case Nominative case refers to a noun or pronoun that is functioning as the subject of a sentence.

EXAMPLES **My brother** and **I** are visiting our grandparents tomorrow.
Mein Bruder und **ich** besuchen morgen unsere Großeltern.

comparison Comparison refers to the inflection of an adjective or adverb to indicate the three degrees of relative intensity: positive, comparative, and superlative.

EXAMPLES She is as **old** as my brother, but **older** than my sister. She is the **oldest** child.
Sie ist so **alt** wie mein Bruder aber **älter** als meine Schwester. Sie ist das **älteste** Kind.

compound nouns Compound nouns are noun combinations that in English may or may not be spelled as one word. In German, compound nouns are always spelled as one word.

EXAMPLES football folk song basketball player
Fußball Volkslied Basketballspieler

conditional mood The conditional mood is used to tell what you *would* or *would not* do under certain conditions, and to express polite requests.

EXAMPLES I **would go** with you if **I had** the time.
Ich **würde** mit dir gehen, wenn ich Zeit **hätte**.
Would you **go** with me tomorrow?
Würdest du morgen mit mir **gehen**?

conjugations Conjugation refers to the inflection of verbs. A verb is conjugated in order to agree with the subject in number.

EXAMPLES We play soccer well, but Mia plays soccer a lot better.
Wir spiel**en** gut Fußball, aber Mia spiel**t** viel besser.

conjunctions Conjunctions are words that connect sentences or clauses.

EXAMPLES I would like to go now, **but** I can't **because** I have no money.
Ich möchte jetzt gehen, **aber** ich kann nicht, **weil** ich kein Geld habe.

contraction A contraction is a shortened form of a word or group of words. Apostrophes in contractions indicate where letters have been omitted.

EXAMPLES **We'd** rather go swimming right now.
Wie **geht's**?
zu + dem = **zum**

dative case (See **case.**)

definite article (See **article.**)

demonstrative adjective A demonstrative adjective points out a person, a place, a thing, or an idea.

EXAMPLES Karen wants **these** shoes and **that** backpack.
Karen möchte **diese** Schuhe und **diesen** Rucksack.

demonstrative pronoun A demonstrative pronoun stands for a specific person, place, thing, or idea.

EXAMPLES **These** are better.
Diese sind besser.

direct object A direct object is a noun or pronoun that receives the action of the verb or shows the result of the action.

EXAMPLES We saw **an opera** and **a play**.
Wir haben **eine Oper** und **ein Hörspiel** gesehen.

direct object pronoun (See **pronoun.**)

gender Gender refers to the classification of German nouns into three categories, or genders: masculine, feminine, and neuter. German nouns can belong to any of the three genders, and there is no logic to it. Gender markers, especially the definite article, are used to indicate to what gender a noun belongs.

the apple	**the** pear	**the** fruit
der Apfel	**die** Birne	**das** Obst

imperative mood A sentence in the imperative mood gives a command or makes a request and is followed by either a period or an exclamation point.

EXAMPLES **Go** shopping. **Let's leave** now!
Geh einkaufen. **Gehen wir** jetzt!

imperfect The imperfect is a form of the past tense in which the conjugated verb changes its form to reflect the past tense.

EXAMPLES I **went** to the park, **bought** ice cream, and **read** a book.
Ich **ging** zum Park, **kaufte** ein Eis und **las** ein Buch.

indefinite article (See **article.**)

indirect object An indirect object is a noun or pronoun that tells to whom or to what, or for whom or for what, the action of the verb is done.

EXAMPLES I bought **my brother** a cell phone.
Ich habe **meinem Bruder** ein Handy gekauft.

indirect object pronoun (See **pronoun.**)

infinitive An infinitive is the form of a verb listed in a dictionary or in your vocabulary. In English, the infinitive is often preceded by the word *to.*

EXAMPLES **To err** is human. **To be** or not **to be**, that is the question.
Irren ist menschlich. **Sein** oder nicht **sein**, das ist die Frage!

inflection Inflection refers to the change of form by which a word indicates certain grammatical elements such as case, gender, or number.

interrogative adjective An interrogative adjective is an adjective that introduces a question.

EXAMPLES **Which** book do you want**?** **Welches** Buch willst du**?**

interrogative pronoun An interrogative pronoun is a word that stands for a noun and introduces a question.

EXAMPLES **Which** (book) do you want**?** **Welches** (Buch) willst du**?**

interrogative sentence An interrogative sentence asks a question and is followed by a question mark.

EXAMPLES Are Sven and Laura going to be home tonight**?**
Sind Sven und Laura heute Abend zu Hause**?**

irregular verb An irregular verb is a verb whose forms do not follow a regular, predictable pattern.

mood Mood is the form a verb takes to indicate the attitude of the speaker. (See also **imperative mood, conditional mood,** and **subjunctive mood.**)

negation Negation refers to the act of denying or giving a negative answer.

EXAMPLES I do **not** hike in the winter. I have **no** money.
Ich wandre **nicht** im Winter. Ich habe **kein** Geld.

nominative case (See **case.**)

noun A noun names a person, place, thing, or idea.

EXAMPLES **Grandpa** has **pictures** of his **trip** to **Spain**.
Opa hat **Fotos** von seiner **Reise** nach **Spanien**.

number Number is the form a word takes to indicate whether it is singular or plural.

EXAMPLES My **sister** bought terrific **jeans** and three **sweaters**.
Meine **Schwester** hat eine tolle **Jeans** und drei **Pullis** gekauft.

passive voice A verb in the passive voice expresses an action done *to* the subject of the sentence.

EXAMPLES The car **is being repaired** by a good mechanic.
Das Auto **wird** von einem guten Mechaniker **repariert**.

possessive adjective A possessive adjective is an adjective that indicates to whom or what something belongs.

EXAMPLES This is **my** pen. That is **his** CD.
Das ist **mein** Kuli. Das ist **seine** CD.

preposition A preposition shows the relationship of a noun or a pronoun to another word in a sentence.

EXAMPLES Lucy bought a cake **for** Sarah's party **at** the market.
Lucy hat **auf** dem Markt eine Torte **für** Saras Fete gekauft.

pronoun A pronoun is used in place of one or more nouns or pronouns. (See also **demonstrative pronoun, interrogative pronoun,** and **relative pronoun.**)

EXAMPLES **Tyler** told **his parents** that **he** would drive **them** to the airport.
Tyler hat **seinen Eltern** gesagt, dass **er sie** zum Flughafen fährt.

direct object pronoun A direct object pronoun is a pronoun that stands for the direct object of a sentence.

EXAMPLES Have you seen **it**? (i.e. my coat)
Hast du **ihn** gesehen? (i.e. meinen Mantel)

indirect object pronoun An indirect object pronoun is a word that stands for the indirect object of a sentence.
EXAMPLES Let's send **them** a postcard. (i.e. our teachers)
Schicken wir **ihnen** eine Karte. (i.e. unseren Lehrern)

subject pronoun A subject pronoun stands for the person or thing that performs the action of the verb.
EXAMPLES **She** plays soccer and **he** watches.
Sie spielt Fußball und **er** sieht zu.

reflexive pronoun A reflexive pronoun indicates that the subject of the sentence also receives the action of the verb.
EXAMPLES The cat sees **itself** in the mirror.
Die Katze sieht **sich** im Spiegel.

reflexive verb A reflexive verb is always used with a reflexive pronoun in certain idiomatic contexts.
EXAMPLES He **injured himself.**
Er hat **sich verletzt.**

regular verb A regular verb is a verb whose forms follow a regular, predictable pattern.

relative pronoun A relative pronoun introduces a clause that refers to another word in the sentence.
EXAMPLES This is a movie **that** I really like.
Das ist ein Film, **den** ich wirklich mag.

subject The subject is the part of a sentence that names the person or thing spoken about in the rest of the sentence.
EXAMPLES **Linda** plays chess with her math teacher.
Linda spielt mit ihrem Mathelehrer Schach.

subject pronoun (See **pronoun.**)

subject-verb agreement (See **agreement.**)

subjunctive mood The subjunctive mood is used to express a suggestion, a necessity, a condition contrary to fact, or a wish.
EXAMPLES If I **were** you, I **would** leave at once.
Wenn ich du **wäre, würde** ich sofort gehen.

tense The tense of verbs indicates the time of the action or state of being that is expressed by the verb.
EXAMPLES I **run.** I **ran.** I **will run.**
Ich **laufe.** Ich **lief.** Ich **werde laufen.**

verb A verb expresses an action or a state of being. (See also **irregular verb, reflexive verb,** and **regular verb.**)
EXAMPLES Evelyn **wears** a blue jacket. **Are** we almost home?
Evelyn **trägt** eine blaue Jacke. **Sind** wir bald zu Hause?

Grammar Tutor Activities
Komm mit!
German 1

KAPITEL 1

QUESTIONS

Pupil's Edition, p. 23

In English A **question** is an interrogative sentence that invites a reply. A question can be formed by using a question word (interrogative) first, followed by a verb, or it can be formed by using the verb first, followed by the subject.

Who is the German teacher?
Is the teacher from Germany?

A. Do these questions begin with an interrogative or a verb? Check the appropriate column.

	INTERROGATIVE	VERB
1. What is your name?	✓	
2. Are you from Boston?		
3. How old are you?		
4. Who rides the bus to school?		
5. Where are you from?		
6. Is his name Ahmet?		
7. Are you from Turkey?		
8. Where is Ahmet from?		
9. Who is the German teacher?		
10. Are you already sixteen?		

In German German questions can also begin with an interrogative or a verb. When a question begins with an interrogative, the verb follows. When a question begins with a verb, the subject follows.

Wer ist der Deutschlehrer?
Ist der Lehrer aus Deutschland?

Woher kommt der Deutschlehrer?
Kommt der Lehrer aus Deutschland?

KAPITEL 1

B. Do these questions begin with an interrogative or a verb? Check the appropriate column.

	INTERROGATIVE	VERB
1. Wie heißt du?	✓	
2. Bist du aus Boston?		
3. Wie alt bist du?		
4. Wer kommt mit dem Bus zur Schule?		
5. Woher bist du?		
6. Heißt er Ahmet?		
7. Kommst du aus der Türkei?		
8. Wer kommt aus Deutschland?		
9. Wer ist die Deutschlehrerin?		
10. Bist du schon sechzehn?		

C. What goes in the blank, a verb or an interrogative? Check the appropriate column. Then fill in the blank with an appropriate verb or interrogative.

	INTERROGATIVE	VERB
1. **Wie** heißt das Mädchen?	✓	
2. ___________ ist sie? Aus Deutschland?		
3. ___________ kommt sie zur Schule?		
4. ___________ sie mit dem Rad zur Schule?		
5. ___________ ist die Deutschlehrerin?		
6. ___________ sie aus Deutschland oder aus Österreich?		
7. ___________ kommt der Ahmet?		
8. ___________ er aus der Türkei?		
9. Und ___________ bist du? Aus der Schweiz?		
10. ___________ Holger aus der Schweiz?		

D. How would you summarize what you have learned about German question formation in your own words?

____

____

____

____

____

In English A **noun** is a word that names something. Here are some examples of nouns. Why are some nouns capitalized?

teacher, boy, Harry, Florida, Miami, bike, school, years, capital, car, bus

A. Underline the nouns in these sentences.

1. This is the teacher.
2. The boy is called Harry.
3. He lives in Miami, Florida.
4. He rides his bike to school.
5. His teacher is Mrs. Schmidt.
6. What is the capital of Florida?
7. Our teacher takes his car to school.
8. I take the bus, and sometimes I take my bike.
9. Christa is from Berlin.
10. She takes the subway to school.

In German Now look at these German nouns. What is one of the main differences between English nouns and German nouns? –**All German nouns are capitalized.**

Lehrer, Junge, Holger, Brandenburg, Potsdam, Rad
Schule, Jahre, Hauptstadt, Sonja, Fuß, Auto

B. Underline the German nouns in these sentences.

1. Das ist der Lehrer.
2. Der Junge heißt Holger.
3. Er wohnt in Potsdam, in Brandenburg.
4. Er kommt mit dem Rad zur Schule.
5. Wer ist das Mädchen?
6. Sie heißt Sonja und ist fünfzehn Jahre alt.
7. Die Mutter bringt mich mit dem Auto zur Schule.
8. Wie heißt die Hauptstadt von Brandenburg?
9. Die Hauptstadt von Brandenburg heißt Potsdam.
10. Die Deutschlehrerin kommt aus Hamburg.

C. Which noun from the box on the preceding page goes into the line provided?

1. Die Hauptstadt von Brandenburg heißt **Potsdam**.
2. Herr Meier ist der ______________________.
3. Wie heißt der ______________________? Holger oder Ahmet?
4. Der Ahmet ist schon 16 ______________________ alt.
5. Wie kommst du zur ______________________?
6. Ich komme mit dem ______________________ zur Schule.
7. Meine Mutter bringt mich mit dem ______________________ zur Schule.
8. Die Sonja kommt zu ______________________ zur Schule.
9. Berlin ist die ______________________ von Deutschland.
10. Das ist die ______________________, ein Mädchen aus Potsdam.

D. What can you say about German nouns in your own words?

____

____

____

DEFINITE ARTICLES

In English The word "the" is called the **definite article**. It is used before nouns when referring to a particular person, thing, or idea. The English definite article does not change in the plural.

The boy is called Ahmet.
The teacher is Frau Weigel.
The girl is fourteen years old.
The girls are called Tara and Steffi.

A. Underline the definite articles in these sentences.

1. Marvin takes the subway to school.
2. The German teacher is from Berlin.
3. Where is the bike?
4. The girl is called Hannah.
5. How old is the boy?
6. When does the bus come?

In German Now study these German sentences. How many different definite articles are there? Name them.

Der Junge heißt Ahmet.
Die Lehrerin ist Frau Weigel.
Das Mädchen ist vierzehn Jahre alt.
Die Mädchen heißen Tara und Steffi.

The definite article has a greater role in German than in English because it shows the gender of the noun with which it is used.

der, as in **der Junge**, indicates that **Junge** is a masculine noun
die, as in **die Lehrerin**, indicates that **Lehrerin** is a feminine noun
das, as in **das Mädchen**, indicates that **Mädchen** is a neuter noun
die is used for all plural nouns; there is no gender in the plural

B. Underline the nouns and circle the definite articles in the following sentences. Then determine if the nouns are masculine, feminine, or neuter. Check the appropriate column.

	MASCULINE	FEMININE	NEUTER
1. Wann kommt der Bus?	✓		
2. Wie alt ist das Moped?			
3. Woher kommt die U-Bahn?			
4. Das Auto ist schon alt.			

5. Wo ist das Rad? ____________ ____________ ____________
6. Wie heißt die Hauptstadt? ____________ ____________ ____________
7. Und wie heißt das Bundesland? ____________ ____________ ____________
8. Woher kommt der Deutschlehrer? ____________ ____________ ____________
9. Woher ist die Biologielehrerin? ____________ ____________ ____________
10. Das Mädchen heißt Anja. ____________ ____________ ____________

C. Write the correct definite article in the space provided. Look above for clues.

1. Wie alt ist ___das___ Auto?
2. Wie alt ist ____________ Mädchen?
3. Wann kommt ____________ Bus?
4. Woher ist ____________ Junge?
5. Wie heißt ____________ Hauptstadt von Brandenburg?
6. Wie heißt ____________ Deutschlehrerin?
7. ____________ Moped ist schon zehn Jahre alt.
8. Ist ____________ Rad neu?
9. Wie alt ist ____________ Biolehrer?

D. How would you summarize what you have learned about the German definite articles?

____

____

____

In English The **subject** is a word or phrase in a sentence that tells us the doer of the action or what is being described or identified. The subject of each sentence is underlined below.

> **The boy** is fifteen years old.
> **He** plays the guitar.
> **The biology teacher** comes from Dresden.

To find the **subject**, first locate the verb. Then ask yourself who or what is performing the action of the verb. The person or thing is the subject of the sentence.

A. Underline the subjects in the following sentences.

1. Where does the teacher live?
2. The girl is from Austria.
3. Where is Mr. Brown from?
4. The student lives in Liechtenstein.
5. Is Jenny riding her moped to school?
6. What is the capital of Germany?
7. Monika is already sixteen.
8. The teacher comes from Austria.
9. How old is Handan?
10. Is she from Turkey?

In German You can find the **subject** of a German sentence the same way you do in English – by locating the person or thing that performs the action of the verb.

> **Der Junge** ist fünfzehn Jahre alt.
> **Die Biologielehrerin** sagt: Guten Morgen.
> **Das Mädchen** kommt aus der Türkei.

Noun phrases that are the **subject** of German sentences are in the **nominative case**

KAPITEL 1

B. Underline the subjects in the following sentences.

1. Wie heißt der Junge?
2. Woher kommt die Deutschlehrerin?
3. Das Auto kommt aus Österreich.
4. Wie heißt die Hauptstadt von Deutschland?
5. Wie alt ist die Biologielehrerin?
6. Der Holger ist auch schon 14 Jahre alt.
7. Der Junge da heißt Stefan, nicht?
8. Der Deutschlehrer ist aus Hessen.
9. Woher ist Annika? Aus Bern?
10. Wo liegt die Hauptstadt von Bayern?

C. For each sentence, write a subject in the space provided. Use a noun and its definite article (**der, die,** or **das**).

1. Wie heißt **das Mädchen**? Heißt sie Tara?
2. Wie heißt ______________________? Heißt er Holger?
3. Wie heißt ______________________ von Deutschland?
4. Herr Meier ist ______________________.
5. Frau Weiß ist ______________________.

D. What can you say about subjects in your own words?

____

____

____

SUBJECT PRONOUNS AND THE VERB *TO BE*

Pupil's Edition, p. 26

In English The **subject** is a word or phrase in a sentence that tells us the doer of the action or what is being described or identified.

> **Brian** is seventeen years old. **He** is from Alabama.
> Where are **you** from?– **I** am from Pennsylvania.
> Where is **Mrs. Johnson** from? – **She** is from New Jersey.

The subject of a sentence can be a noun or a **pronoun**. A pronoun is a word used in place of a noun (or a group of nouns).

A. Underline the subjects in the following English sentences.

1. Steven is fifteen years old.
2. I am sixteen years old.
3. We are from Kentucky.
4. Where is Mary from?
5. She is from Virginia.
6. The biology teacher is from New York.
7. Where are you from, Kirsten?
8. Where are you from, Alex and Julia?
9. We are from Erfurt.
10. Is Stefan also from Erfurt?

In German Now look at these German sentences and notice the subject pronouns.

> **Brian** ist siebzehn Jahre alt. **Er** ist aus Alabama.
> Woher bist **du**? – **Ich** bin aus Pennsylvania.
> Woher ist **Frau Johnson**? – **Sie** ist aus New Jersey.

B. Underline the subjects in the following German sentences.

1. Stefan ist fünfzehn Jahre alt.
2. Ich bin sechzehn Jahre alt.
3. Wir sind aus Kentucky.
4. Woher ist Mary?
5. Ich glaube, sie ist aus Virginia.
6. Der Biologielehrer ist aus New York.
7. Woher bist du, Kirsten?
8. Woher seid ihr, Alex und Julia?
9. Wir kommen aus Erfurt.
10. Kommt der Stefan auch aus Erfurt?

C. If you underlined the subjects correctly for both the English and the German examples, what do you notice?

____

____

The Verb **sein**, *to be*

D. Write the English forms of the verb *to be* that you see in Activity A.

____

E. Write the equivalent German forms of **sein**, *to be.*

____

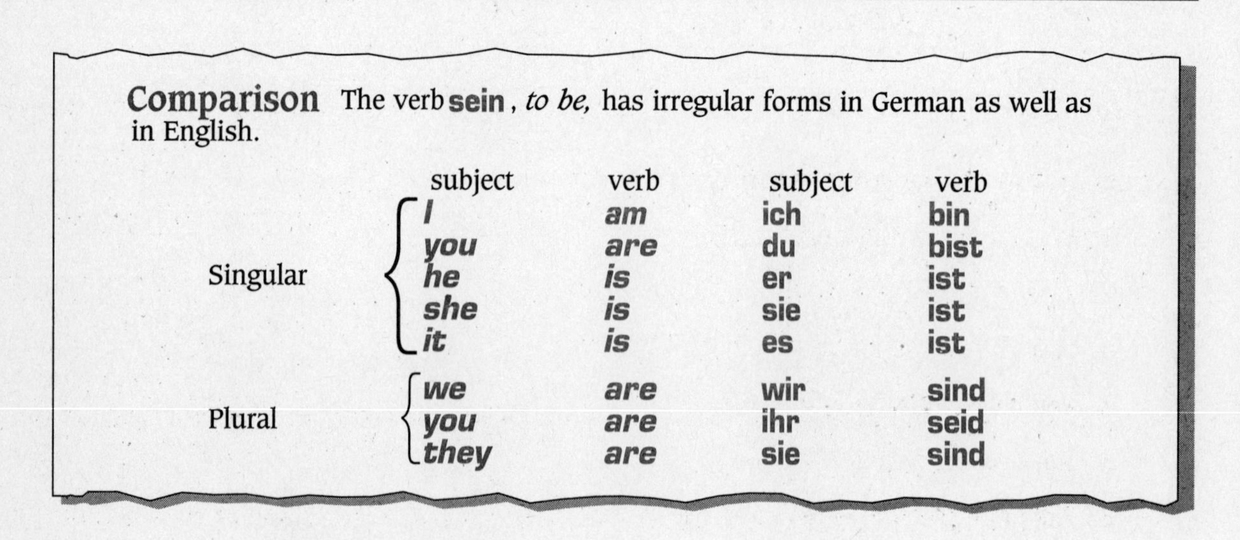

Comparison The verb **sein**, *to be,* has irregular forms in German as well as in English.

	subject	verb	subject	verb
Singular	*I*	*am*	ich	bin
	you	*are*	du	bist
	he	*is*	er	ist
	she	*is*	sie	ist
	it	*is*	es	ist
Plural	*we*	*are*	wir	sind
	you	*are*	ihr	seid
	they	*are*	sie	sind

F. Underline the forms of **sein** first, and then fill in the blanks with the missing pronoun.

1. Wir sind aus Michigan. Und woher seid ___ihr___ ?
2. Mark ist aus Wisconsin und ______________ ist 16 Jahre alt.
3. Barbara ist aus Idaho und ______________ ist schon 17 Jahre alt.
4. Dylan und James sind aus Texas; ______________ sind aus Plano.
5. Rick und Abe sind aus Arkansas; ______________ sind aus Little Rock.
6. Ich bin aus Illinois. Und woher bist ______________ ?
7. Du bist aus Los Angeles und ______________ bin aus Milwaukee.
8. Ihr seid aus New York und ______________ sind aus New Jersey.

G. How would you summarize what you know about the German verb **sein** in your own words?

____

____

____

SUBJECTS AND VERBS

Pupil's Edition, p. 52

In English A **verb** is a word that expresses action or a state of being.

Anne **plays** tennis well.
She **is** twelve years old.

A. Underline the verbs in each of the following sentences.

1. We listen to a lot of music.
2. Tara is not home.
3. She swims in the afternoon.
4. You collect stamps?
5. No, I collect comics.
6. Adam and Susan watch TV in the evening.
7. In the fall I hike a lot.
8. I play guitar and piano.
9. We hike on weekends.
10. I read a lot.

In German Now look at these German sentences. In what position is the verb?

Anna **spielt** gut Tennis.
Sie **ist** zwölf Jahre alt.

In German sentences the verb is generally in second position. The subject usually comes first, but not always! Other elements can also precede the verb. When this happens, the subject comes after the verb.

B. Underline the verbs in each of the following German sentences.

1. Wir hören viel Musik.
2. Tara ist nicht zu Hause.
3. Sie schwimmt am Nachmittag.
4. Du sammelst Briefmarken?
5. Nein, ich sammle Comics.
6. Adam und Susan schauen am Abend Fernsehen.
7. Im Herbst wandre ich viel.
8. Ich spiele Gitarre und Klavier.
9. Wir wandern am Wochenende.
10. Ich lese viel.

C. Looking at the endings of the verbs, what is the difference between the English verb pattern and the German verb pattern?

____

____

____

CONJUGATION OF VERBS

In English The term **conjugation** refers to the possible forms of a verb for each of the pronouns. Conjugations are always listed with pronouns.

I	swim.	We swim.
You	swim.	You swim.
He / She / It	swims.	They swim.

A. Underline the subjects and circle the verbs.

1. You play the piano, right?
2. Tara plays tennis very well.
3. Tara and Steffi play together often.
4. We play tennis only on the weekend.
5. The boys and girls play tennis together.
6. Holger plays tennis with his coach.
7. I play tennis whenever I can.

B. How many different verb forms does the conjugation of an English verb such as *to play* above have?

____

Compare Look at the English conjugation of the verb *to play* and compare it to the German conjugation of the verb **spielen**.

Singular	*I*	*play*	ich	spiel**e**
	you	*play*	du	spiel**st**
	he	*play***s**	er	spiel**t**
	she	*play***s**	sie	spiel**t**
	it	*play***s**	es	spiel**t**
Plural	*we*	*play*	wir	spiel**en**
	you	*play*	ihr	spiel**t**
	they	*play*	sie	spiel**en**

How many different verb forms does the German conjugation have? What part of the verb changes, and what part stays the same?

C. Underline the subjects and circle the verbs.

1. Du spielst Klavier, ja?
2. Tara spielt sehr gut Tennis.
3. Tara und Steffi spielen oft.
4. Wir spielen Tennis am Wochenende.
5. Die Jungen und Mädchen spielen Tennis.
6. Holger spielt Tennis mit dem Trainer.
7. Ich spiele auch Tennis.

D. How many different verb forms does the conjugation of a German verb such as *spielen* have?

____

E. What pronouns can be used with each of the German verb forms?

1. **spielen** can be used with **wir, sie** ________________
2. **spielt** can be used with ________________
3. **spiele** can be used with ________________
4. **spielst** can be used with ________________

KAPITEL 2

F. Write the correct pronoun that goes with each verb.

1. Was machst **du** in deiner Freizeit?
2. ________ zeichne und ________ sammle Briefmarken.
3. Und was macht ________, Maria und Johannes?
4. ________ schauen Fernsehen und ________ hören Musik.
5. Was machen Holger und Tara? – ________ spielen Tennis.
6. Und ________ glaube, ________ spielen auch Volleyball.
7. Was macht ________ nach der Schule, Mark und Sarah?
8. ________ schwimmen. ________ finden Schwimmen toll!

G. How would you summarize what you have learned about the conjugation of German verbs?

____

____

____

SUBJECT-VERB AGREEMENT

Pupil's Edition, p. 52

In English A verb must agree in number with its subject.

Tara **plays** tennis today. Singular subjects take **singular verbs**.
Tara and Steffi **play** tennis today. Plural subjects take **plural verbs**.

A. Read each of the following sentences. Then check the appropriate column indicating whether the subject and verb are singular or plural.

	Singular	Plural
1. Jens and Ahmet are playing cards.		✓
2. They are playing Mau-Mau.		
3. What are you doing in your free time, Steffi?		
4. I collect stamps.		
5. In the winter we ski a lot.		
6. Holger has other interests.		
7. Do you play tennis, Mr. Meyer?		
8. Mrs. Meyer likes to swim.		

In German Now look at these German sentences.

Tara **spielt** heute Tennis. Singular subjects take **singular verbs**.
Tara und Steffi **spielen** heute Tennis. Plural subjects take **plural verbs**.

B. Underline the subject and circle the verb in these German sentences. Then check the appropriate column indicating whether the subject and verb are singular or plural.

	Singular	Plural
1. Jens und Ahmet spielen Karten.		✓
2. Sie spielen Mau-Mau.		
3. Was machst du in deiner Freizeit, Steffi?		
4. Ich sammle Briefmarken.		
5. Im Winter laufen wir viel Ski.		
6. Holger hat andere Interessen.		
7. Spielen Sie Tennis, Herr Meyer?		
8. Frau Meyer schwimmt gern.		

C. Write the correct singular form of the verb in parentheses.

1. (sammeln) ___**Sammelst**___ du Comics, Heiko?
2. (sammeln) Nein, ich ______________ Briefmarken.
3. (spielen) Die Annika ______________ gern Karten.
4. (spielen) ______________ der Jens Schach?
5. (wandern) Du ______________ viel im Sommer.
6. (wandern) Herr Schneider ______________ auch viel.
7. (tanzen) Werner ______________ gern.
8. (tanzen) ______________ Marta auch gern?
9. (hören) ______________ du oft Musik?
10. (hören) Ja, ich ______________ Musik nach der Schule.

D. Write the correct plural form of the verb in parentheses.

1. (spielen) Holger, Lisa und Steffi ___**spielen**___ gern Mau-Mau.
2. (wandern) ______________ ihr nicht im Winter, Jens und Ahmet?
3. (sammeln) Wir ______________ Briefmarken.
4. (spielen) Handan und ich ______________ ein Instrument.
5. (spielen) Tara und Steffi? Sie ______________ Klavier.
6. (machen) Karin und du, ihr ______________ viel Hausaufgaben.
7. (besuchen) Ja, und wir ______________ oft Freunde.
8. (zeichnen) Elke und ich ______________ sehr gern.

KAPITEL 2

E. Write the correct form of the verb in parentheses in the space provided. Look for the subject to help you decide which verb form to use.

1. (spielen) Wann ___**spielt**___ Tara Tennis?
2. (spielen) Wann ______________ Tara und Steffi Tennis?
3. (hören) Wann ______________ du Musik?
4. (hören) Wann ______________ ihr Musik, Holger und Steffi?
5. (zeichnen) Der Junge ______________ am Abend.
6. (zeichnen) Mark und John ______________ am Abend.
7. (besuchen) ______________ du Freunde am Wochenende?
8. (wandern) Im Sommer ______________ ich viel.

F. What is meant by subject and verb agreement?

____

In English **Person** refers to any of the three types of subject pronouns that distinguish between the speaker (first person), the individual being addressed (second person), and the individual or thing spoken of (third person).

Number refers to the form that a word takes when it is singular or plural.

The first person, the speaker, can be:
a. an individual speaking for himself: "**I** like playing tennis with Joel."
b. an individual speaking for two or more: "**We** also have other interests."

The second person, the individual addressed, can be:
a. one person to whom you are speaking: "What are **you** doing this afternoon?"
b. more than one person to whom you are speaking: "Brian and Mike, what are **you** doing?"

The third person, the person or thing spoken of, can be:
a. a reference to one male (Mike): **He** likes to listen to music.
b. a reference to one female (Ann): **She** plays tennis with Kristina.
c. a reference to an object or a thing (tennis): **It** is interesting.
d. a reference to more than one person or object (Mike and Ann): **They** are super!

It is convenient to arrange person and number in the following way:

	singular	*singular*	*plural*	*plural*
first person	I	play	we	play
second person	you	play	you	play
third person	he, she, it	play**s**	they	play

In German **Person** and **number** apply to German as well. In German, you can also look at the verb conjugation in order to tell if the subject is singular or plural. Study the following German verb paradigm:

	singular	*singular*	*plural*	*plural*
first person	ich	spiel**e**	wir	spiel**en**
second person	du	spiel**st**	ihr	spiel**t**
third person	er, sie, es	spiel**t**	sie	spiel**en**

A. English: If "to play" is the basic form of the verb, or the **infinitive**, which person shows a different form, and what is this form?

___

KAPITEL 2

B. German: If "spielen" is the basic form of the verb, or the **infinitive**, which persons show a different form, and what are these forms?

____

____

C. Complete the following sentences using German subjects and verbs.

1. I play tennis with Mike. ___**Ich**___ ___**spiele**___ Tennis mit Mike.
2. You play cards. ________ ____________ Karten.
3. He plays in the afternoon. ________ ____________ am Nachmittag.
4. She plays soccer. ________ ____________ Fußball.
5. We play after school. ________ ____________ nach der Schule.
6. Tara and Steffi play tennis. ________ ____________ Tennis.
7. They play in the evening. ________ ____________ am Abend.

D. Fill in each blank with the correct pronoun or verb form.

1. Was ___**machst**___ ___**du**___ nach der Schule, Holger?
2. ________ ____________ mit Steffi und Tara Tennis.
3. Was ____________ die Mädchen nach der Schule?
4. ________ glaube, sie ____________ auch Tennis.
5. Was ____________ Herr Meier in seiner Freizeit?
6. ________ ____________ Briefmarken.
7. Sag, ____________ du auch Sport, Heike?
8. Du, ________ schwimme, und ________ ____________ Klavier.

E. How would you summarize what you have learned about person and number of subject pronouns in relation to verbs?

____

____

____

KAPITEL 2

PRESENT TENSE

In English The **tense** of a verb indicates the relative time of the action or state of being. The following sentences are three examples of tenses in English.

Tara **plays** tennis after school.	present tense
School **started** at 8 o'clock.	past tense
We **will play** soccer on the weekend.	future tense

The **present tense** is used to indicate **present time**. In English there are three present-tense forms that indicate present time:

Tara **plays** tennis after school.	present tense – regular
She **is playing** with Steffi today.	present tense – progressive
She **does play** very well.	present tense – emphatic

A. Underline the present-tense verb forms in these English sentences.

1. I do visit friends on the weekend.
2. And you are playing soccer.
3. Steffi lives in Germany.
4. She does play tennis very well.
5. Holger finds tennis boring.
6. He is playing the guitar.
7. We do play soccer on the weekend.
8. Bobby and Rick, you are playing cards in the evening.
9. They also play volleyball on the weekend.
10. Taylor and I are playing chess.

In German There is one present-tense form to indicate present time. There is no progressive nor emphatic present tense.

Tara **plays** Tennis after school.	Tara **spielt** Tennis nach der Schule.
She **is playing** tennis after school.	Sie **spielt** Tennis nach der Schule.
She **does play** tennis after school.	Sie **spielt** Tennis nach der Schule.

B. Underline the present-tense verb forms in these German sentences.

1. Ich besuche Freunde am Wochenende.
2. Und du spielst Fußball.
3. Steffi wohnt in Deutschland.
4. Sie spielt ja sehr gut Tennis.
5. Holger findet Tennis langweilig.
6. Er spielt Gitarre.
7. Wir spielen am Wochenende Fußball.
8. Bobby und Rick, ihr spielt Karten am Abend.
9. Sie spielen auch Volleyball am Wochenende.
10. Taylor und ich spielen Schach.

C. Write the English verb forms from Exercise A on the lines below.

____

____

D. How many different categories of the present tense do you find in English? List them.

____

____

E. Write the German verb forms from Exercise B on the lines below.

____

____

F. What is the difference between the English present tense and the German present tense?

____

____

WORD ORDER: POSITION OF THE VERB IN A STATEMENT

Pupil's Edition, p. 56

In English **Word order** refers to the position of various elements in a sentence.

Each of the following sentences consists of three elements: a subject, a verb, and a time expression. In what position is the verb?

Mark jogs after school.
In the evening he draws.

A. Underline the verb in each sentence, then circle the subject.

1. (We) are playing soccer after school.
2. In the evening we are playing tennis.
3. After school I am doing my homework.
4. Holger does homework in the evening.
5. In the evening Mark and Matt watch television.
6. In the fall we hike a lot.

B. Now answer the following questions.

1. In what position is the subject in relation to the verb? ____________________
2. What element precedes the subject in the second sentence? ____________________

In German Read these German sentences and look at the position of the verb.

Position	1	2	3	4
	Rob	joggt	nach der Schule.	
	Am Abend	zeichnet	er.	
	Tennis	finde	ich	prima.

In simple German sentences the verb is always in second position. It can be preceded by the subject or by another element, such as a time expression (**am Abend**) or any other word (**Tennis**).

KAPITEL 2

C. Underline the verb in each sentence, then circle the subject.

1. Wir spielen nach der Schule Fußball.
2. Am Abend spielen wir Tennis.
3. Tennis spielen wir am Abend.
4. Nach der Schule mache ich Hausaufgaben.
5. Holger macht die Hausaufgaben am Abend.
6. Am Abend schauen Mark und Matt Fernsehen.
7. Im Herbst wandern wir viel.
8. Die Schüler finden Deutsch einfach.

D. Now answer the following questions.

1. In what position is the subject in relation to the verb? ______________________
2. What element precedes the subject in the second sentence? ______________________

E. Now circle the subject and underline the verb in the following sentences. Then rewrite each sentence by beginning with the expression in italics.

1. Ich jogge *am Nachmittag.* **Am Nachmittag jogge ich.**
2. Wir spielen *im Sommer* Tennis. ______________________
3. Wir finden *Deutsch* einfach. ______________________
4. Sabine hört *am Abend* Musik. ______________________
5. Ich spiele *nach der Schule* Klavier. ______________________
6. Wir spielen nach der Schule *Golf.* ______________________
7. Ich finde *Tennis* super. ______________________
8. Wir wandern gern *im Herbst.* ______________________

F. What have you learned about word order in German sentences?

1. What element can be in first position? ______________________
2. In what position is the verb? ______________________
3. In what position can the subject be? ______________________
4. When is the subject in third position? ______________________

G. How would you summarize what you have learned about German word order?

____

____

KAPITEL 3

MODAL VERBS: THE MÖCHTE-FORMS

Pupil's Edition, p. 75

In English A **modal auxiliary verb** belongs to a set of English verbs such as *can, could, may, might, must, shall, should, would* that are used with another verb, the main verb, to express mood or possibility.

You **may** eat a piece of cake. [modal verb: **may**, main verb: eat]
He **would** drink a cola. [modal verb: **would**, main verb: drink]

A. In the following sentences, circle the modal verb and underline the main verb.

1. Juan would eat a piece of cake.
2. Katie may have fruit.
3. We can drink a glass of orange juice.
4. I must drink apple juice.
5. Holger may visit his friend.
6. Steffi should drink a cola.
7. Jens and Steffi would take a few cookies.
8. Mr. Moser could live in the country.
9. We might visit friends.
10. I should buy the car.

In German Modal auxiliary verbs are called **modal verbs**, or simply **modals**. There are six modal verbs in German. The **möchte**-forms, *would like,* are the first modal you will learn.

Ich **möchte** ein Glas Wasser trinken.	*I would like a glass of water to drink.*
Ich **möchte** ein Glas Wasser.	*I would like a glass of water.*
Möchtest du eine Cola trinken?	*Would you like a cola to drink?*

Notice that in German, the modal verb and the main verb are separated. The modal verb (like other conjugated verbs) is in the normal verb position, while the main verb is used at the end of the sentence. You can also use the modal by itself, without a main verb.

Here is the conjugation of **möchte**. How is it different from other verb conjugations you have learned?

ich	möcht**e**	wir	möcht**en**
du	möcht**est**	ihr	möcht**et**
er/sie/es	möcht**e**	sie/Sie	möcht**en**

B. In the following German sentences, circle the modal verb (the **möchte**-form) and underline the main verb, if any.

1. Holger (möchte) ein Stück Kuchen essen.
2. Möchtest du eine Limo trinken?
3. Wir möchten ein Glas Orangensaft trinken.
4. Was möchte Holger essen?
5. Holger möchte ein paar Kekse essen.
6. Steffi möchte eine Cola trinken.
7. Jens und ich möchten ein paar Kekse.
8. Herr Moser möchte auf dem Land wohnen.
9. Möchte Inge Freunde besuchen?
10. Ich möchte das Auto.

C. Write the correct **möchte**-form in the in the space provided.

1. Was ______**möchtest**______ du, Kuchen oder Kekse?
2. Ich ____________________ Obst und ein Glas Saft, bitte.
3. Was ____________________ ihr, Tara und Jens?
4. Wir ____________________ eine Cola und ein Glas Wasser.
5. Was ____________________ Ahmet essen?
6. Ahmet ____________________ nichts essen.
7. Und was ____________________ Sie, Frau Schirmer?
8. Herr Langer ____________________ eine Tasse Kaffee.
9. ____________________ du ein Glas Mineralwasser, Emil?
10. Karl und Birgit, was ____________________ ihr essen?

D. In what position is the **möchte**-form, and in what position is the main verb?

möchte-form: ____________________ main verb: ____________________

E. What can you say about the **möchte**-forms in your own words?

____

____

In English The **third-person pronouns** *he, she, it,* and *they* are used to refer to persons and things. Pronouns can replace nouns or noun phrases (such as noun and article).

Nouns	*Pronouns*
Mr. Gärtner is not old.	He is not old.
Mrs. Weigel is fifty.	She is fifty.
The desk is new.	It is new.
The stereo is broken.	It is broken.
The room is big.	It is big.
The chairs are old.	They are old.

A. Underline the noun phrase in the first sentence and circle the pronoun that refers to that noun phrase in the second sentence.

1. What is the boy called? —He is called Ahmet.
2. How old is the armoire? — It is forty years old.
3. How big is the shelf? — It is not very big.
4. Is the couch new? — Yes, it is new, quite new.
5. Is Mrs. Weigel the biology teacher? — Yes, she is the biology teacher.
6. Is the apple juice good? — Yes, it is good.

In German All German nouns have gender. They are either masculine, feminine, or neuter. A pronoun that replaces a German noun must be the same gender as the noun. In these sentences the pronouns are the **subject** of the sentence.

Herr Gärtner ist nicht alt.	**Er** ist nicht alt.	(masculine, singular)
Frau Weigel ist fünfzig.	**Sie** ist fünfzig.	(feminine, singular)
Der Schreibtisch ist neu.	**Er** ist neu.	(masculine, singular)
Die Stereoanlage ist kaputt.	**Sie** ist kaputt.	(feminine, singular)
Das Zimmer ist groß.	**Es** ist groß.	(neuter, singular)
Die Stühle sind alt.	**Sie** sind alt.	(plural)

Looking at the German and English sentences above, the English pronoun *it* has three German equivalents: **er**, **sie**, and **es**.

B. Underline the noun phrase and circle the pronoun that refers back to the noun phrase in these German sentences.

1. Wie heißt der Junge? –Er heißt Ahmet.
2. Wie alt ist der Schrank? – Er ist vierzig Jahre alt.
3. Wie groß ist das Regal? – Es ist nicht sehr groß.

4. Ist die Couch neu? – Ja, sie ist neu, ganz neu.
5. Ist Frau Weigel die Biologielehrerin? – Ja, sie ist die Biologielehrerin.
6. Ist der Apfelsaft gut? – Ja, er ist gut.
7. Das Regal ist groß. – Ja, es ist sehr groß.
8. Der Stuhl ist sehr unbequem. – Ja, und er ist auch kaputt.
9. Ist der Computer neu? – Ja, er ist ganz neu.

C. What do these pronouns refer to – a masculine noun, a feminine noun, a neuter noun, or a plural noun? Check the appropriate column.

	MASCULINE	FEMININE	NEUTER	PLURAL
1. Sie ist schon kaputt.	______	✓	______	______
2. Wie groß sind sie?	______	______	______	______
3. Ist er ganz neu?	______	______	______	______
4. Ja, es ist sehr unbequem!	______	______	______	______
5. Ich glaube, sie sind sehr alt.	______	______	______	______
6. Er ist sehr hässlich.	______	______	______	______
7. Sie sind so bequem!	______	______	______	______
8. Sie ist neu und so schön.	______	______	______	______

D. Underline the noun phrase in the first sentence, then fill in each blank with a pronoun that refers to the preceding noun phrase.

1. Ist die Couch im Zimmer? – Ja, ____sie____ ist im Zimmer.
2. Wie groß ist der Stuhl? – Ich glaube, ______________ ist nicht sehr groß.
3. Wo wohnen Jens und Holger? – Ich glaube, ______________ wohnen in Potsdam.
4. Der Orangensaft ist nicht gut. – Ja, ich glaube, ______________ ist schon sehr alt.
5. Was macht denn die Tara? – Du, ______________ spielt mit Steffi Tennis.
6. Das Regal ist zu klein. – Nein, ich glaube nicht, dass ______________ zu klein ist.
7. Wo ist denn der Kuchen? – Schau, hier ist ______________ !
8. Woher ist der Schreibtisch? – Du, ______________ ist von meinem Opa.

E. What can you say about German subject pronouns in your own words?

____

____

KAPITEL 4

NOUNS AND THEIR PLURAL FORMS

Pupil's Edition, p. 114

In English Number refers to the designation of a word as singular or plural. A noun that refers to one person or thing is **singular**, such as *child, book;* a noun that refers to more than one person or thing is **plural**, such as *children, books.*

In English the plural can be formed in several ways:

a. add **-s**, **-es**, or **-ies** to the noun: book – book**s**, dish – dish**es**, city – cit**ies**
b. change the spelling: man – **men**, goose – **geese**
c. change nothing: fish – **fish**, deer – **deer**

A. Underline all plural nouns.

1. Two men have been playing tennis for the past two days.
2. There are more fish in the bay now than in 1980.
3. Books for children can be expensive.
4. Mice make cheap pets.
5. Several dignitaries are in the audience.
6. All of the money is invested in bonds.

In German German has many different ways to form plurals. Look at these examples:

Heft – Heft**e**
Buch – B**ü**ch**er**
Kuli – Kuli**s**
Schultasche – Schultasche**n**
Taschenrechner – Taschenrechner (same form)

Since you cannot predict the plural form of a new noun you learn, you should always memorize the gender and plural form of German nouns. Here are some common ways to form German plural nouns.

Singular	Plural	Change
das Heft	die Heft**e**	add -**e**
der Schrank	die Schr**ä**nk**e**	add -**e** and umlaut
der Junge	die Junge**n**	add -**n**
das Bett	die Bett**en**	add -**en**
das Buch	die Büch**er**	add -**er** and umlaut
das Zimmer	die Zimmer	no change
der Bruder	die Br**ü**der	add an umlaut
der Kuli	die Kuli**s**	add -**s**

There are many German nouns whose plural forms are predictable. These are nouns ending in -**ung**, -**heit**, and -**keit** that always add -**en**, and nouns ending in -**nis** that always add -**se** to the singular form.

KAPITEL 4

B. Are these nouns singular or plural, or both? Check the correct column.

	SINGULAR	PLURAL	BOTH
1. Wörterbücher		✓	
2. Kuli			
3. Kassetten			
4. Zimmer			
5. Hefte			
6. Stundenplan			
7. Fächer			
8. Väter			
9. Onkel			

In German You do not have to know the plural form of every noun to know whether the noun is singular or plural. The verb form will tell you if the noun is singular or plural. The article is another clue: **der** or **das** nouns change to **die** in the plural.

Wie teuer **ist** die Kassette?	ist: singular
Wie teuer **sind** die Kassetten?	sind: plural
Das Heft **kostet** nur 40 Cent.	das, kostet: singular
Die Hefte **kosten** 80 Cent.	die, kosten: plural

C. Underline all singular noun phrases and circle all plural noun phrases in these German sentences. Make sure you look closely at the verb forms.

1. Holger hat ein Mädchen gern. Mädchen haben Holger gern.
2. Der Taschenrechner ist teuer. – Ja, Taschenrechner sind teuer.
3. Wie teuer sind Bleistifte? Und wie teuer ist das Heft?
4. Meine Schwestern heißen Cindy und Pam. Wie heißt deine Schwester?
5. Die Kassette kostet 1 Euro, und die Kassetten da kosten nur 50 Cent.
6. Die Wörterbücher sind teuer, aber das Wörterbuch da ist preiswert.
7. Das Zimmer ist sehr schön, und die Zimmer da vorn sind super!
8. Mein Bruder ist 17, und Eriks Brüder sind schon 20 und 21 Jahre alt.

D. How would you summarize in your own words what you have learned about the plural form of German nouns?

____

____

____

KAPITEL 5

DIRECT OBJECTS

Pupil's Edition, p. 135

In English **Case** signals how certain nouns or noun phrases function in a sentence. In English, the word order determines the function of a noun phrase in a sentence.

a. A noun phrase can be the **subject** of a sentence.

The T-shirt looks great. (subject, singular)
The T-shirts look great. (subject, plural)

b. A noun phrase can function as the **direct object** of a sentence. The **direct object** is the recipient of the action expressed by the verb. In the following sentences the underlined noun phrases function as the direct object.

I'm buying the T-shirt. Would you like the shirt? I find the shirt cool.

A. Underline the subject noun phrases and circle the direct object noun phrases.

1. That girl would like to buy (the sweater.)
2. Is Mark buying the shirt?
3. No, my friend is buying the shoes.
4. The shoes cost 80 euros.
5. The children also need tennis shoes.
6. My brother will take the sweater.

KAPITEL 5

In German Different forms of the article can signal different functions of a noun phrase. The different functions are called **cases**. **Subjects** are said to be in the **nominative case**, while most **direct objects** are in the **accusative case**.

From the following chart you can see that subject and direct object are clearly signalled when the noun is masculine: **den**, **einen**.

	Noun Phrase as Subject (Nominative)	*Noun Phrase as Direct Object (Accusative)*
Masculine	**Der Pulli** ist toll.	Ich kaufe **den Pulli**.
Feminine	**Die Bluse** passt gut.	Ich möchte **die Bluse**.
Neuter	**Das T-Shirt** ist schick.	Ich kaufe **das T-Shirt**.
Masculine	**Ein Pulli** passt nicht.	Ich suche **einen Pulli**.
Feminine	**Eine Bluse** ist kaputt.	Ich brauche **eine Bluse**.
Neuter	**Ein T-Shirt** ist fesch.	Ich möchte **ein T-Shirt**.

B. Underline the subjects and circle the direct objects in these German sentences.

1. Ich brauche eine Hose; die Hose hier sieht toll aus.
2. Ich suche einen Pulli in Braun; der Pulli hier ist nicht teuer.
3. Der Gürtel ist zu lang; ich brauche einen Gürtel – ja, aber in Schwarz, bitte.
4. Hier ist ein Gürtel in Schwarz, aber der Gürtel kostet 20 Euro.
5. Haben Sie einen Wunsch? – Ich brauche Turnschuhe.
6. Die Bluse ist nicht teuer. Gut, ich kaufe die Bluse.
7. Schau, der Taschenrechner ist billig. Ich brauche einen Taschenrechner.
8. Suchst du den Kuli? – Nein, ich habe den Kuli.

C. Write the correct form of the definite article in the space provided.

1. Der Pulli ist toll und preiswert. Ich kaufe ___den___ Pulli.
2. Die Hemden gefallen mir. Gut, ich kaufe ____________ Hemden.
3. Das T-Shirt ist super. Ich möchte aber ____________ T-Shirt in Blau.
4. Der Rock sieht schick aus. Ja, ich nehme ____________ Rock.
5. Das Kleid ist billig. Ich kaufe ____________ Kleid.
6. Die Bluse ist zu teuer. Ich nehme ____________ Bluse nicht.
7. Der Rock passt prima. Ja, ich kaufe ____________ Rock.
8. Die Jeans und der Gürtel sehen toll aus. Gut, dann nehme ich ____________ Gürtel.

D. Write the correct form of the indefinite article in the space provided.

1. Der Pullover ist preiswert. Ich brauche ___einen___ Pullover.
2. Die Jacke gefällt mir. Ich suche ____________ Jacke.
3. Das Hemd ist so preiswert. Ich möchte ____________ Hemd, aber in Blau!
4. Der Rock sieht toll aus. Ich brauche ____________ Rock, aber nicht so teuer.
5. Die Hose passt gut, aber ich suche ____________ Hose in Grau.
6. Das T-Shirt sieht scheußlich aus. Aber ich brauche ____________ T-Shirt.
7. Der Gürtel ist kaputt! Mutti, ich brauche ____________ Gürtel!

E. How would you summarize what you have learned about direct objects in your own words?

____

____

SUBJECT AND DIRECT OBJECT (NOUN PHRASES)

In English An English sentence relies on word order for meaning. Compare these two sentences:

a. Chris calls up Ann.
b. Ann calls up Chris.

The meaning of each sentence is completely dependent on word order. The **subject** (the caller) is always the first noun phrase. The **direct object** (the person being called) always comes later in the sentence.

A. Underline the subject and circle the direct object (if any) in each sentence.

1. Do you have the sweater in black?
2. Isn't this belt awful?
3. I would like a sweater in blue, please.
4. I don't need a jogging suit.
5. How do you like my skirt?
6. Your skirt looks great!
7. And your blouse is also cute!

In German In a German sentence, the subject does not have to be in the first position. German sentences can begin with the direct object, for emphasis, especially when the context is clear.

Den Pulli kaufe ich nicht, er ist zu teuer.
Das Kleid finde ich einfach toll!
Die Bluse in Weiß habe ich nicht mehr.

What case (nominative or accusative) is the noun phrase in each sentence? How do you know what is the subject and what is the direct object?

Now compare these pairs of sentences.

(Whom does he see?)
a. **Der** Chris sieht die Monika. — Die Monika sieht **der** Chris. (**sehen**-*to see)*

(Whom does she see?)
b. **Den** Chris sieht die Monika. — Die Monika sieht **den** Chris.

Each pair of sentences means the same thing. Notice that in German, the word order can change without affecting the meaning of the sentence. That's why knowing about case is so important — it may be the only thing that tells you what the sentence really means.

In a sentence such as **Die Ann sieht die Monika,** most Germans assume that **die Ann** is the subject and **die Monika** is the direct object. However, context is necessary to make that determination.

B. Underline the subjects and circle the direct objects in the following sentences.

1. Ich finde den Gürtel ein bisschen zu kurz.
2. Den Gürtel finde ich auch zu teuer.
3. Das Hemd nehme ich; ich finde das Hemd einfach toll!
4. Die Bluse kaufe ich nicht. Die Bluse gefällt mir nicht.
5. Sie zieht nur schwarze Klamotten an. Schwarze Klamotten findet sie schick.
6. Die Jeans brauche ich nicht. Die Jeans ist auch zu groß.
7. Dein Rock ist ja super, und deinen Gürtel finde ich auch hübsch.

C. Read the following statements and questions and determine what gender (masculine, feminine, neuter) the noun would be in the blank. Then fill in the blanks to create logical sentences.

	noun		
	MASC.	FEM.	NEUT.
1. Den **Pulli** kaufe ich nicht.	✓	___	___
2. Die ___ findest du toll?	___	___	___
3. Das ___ findet er zu lang.	___	___	___
4. Ein ___ brauche ich nicht.	___	___	___
5. Eine ___ möchtest du kaufen?	___	___	___
6. Einen ___ suche ich.	___	___	___

D. Rewrite the following sentences, beginning each one with the direct object.

1. Ich kaufe die Jacke nicht. **Die Jacke kaufe ich nicht.**
2. Wir finden den Pulli stark. ___
3. Rosi zieht die Stiefel nicht an. ___
4. Ich finde den Rock echt stark. ___
5. Rosi braucht die Klamotten nicht. ___
6. Ich suche die Turnschuhe. ___
7. Katja findet das T-Shirt scheußlich. ___
8. Michael findet das Hemd echt super. ___

E. In your own words, summarize what case means and why case is important in German sentences.

___

___

In English **Direct object pronouns** take the place of nouns or noun phrases that are the direct object of a sentence.

referring to people:	I like Michael.	I like **him**.
	I like Julia.	I like **her**.
	I like Michael and Julia.	I like **them**.
referring to things:	I like the sweater.	I like **it**.
	I like the jacket.	I like **it**.
	I like the shirt.	I like **it**.
	I like the shoes.	I like **them**.

A. Underline the subject and circle the direct object in each sentence.

1. Does Scott like the sweater?
2. No, it doesn't suit him.
3. I find it cool.
4. Then you should buy it.
5. Do they have sweaters in red?
6. They only have them in black.
7. My sister visits her once a week.
8. My parents would like it in dark blue.

In German Look at these German sentences and identify the noun phrases and the corresponding direct object pronouns.

referring to people:	Ich habe Michael gern.	Ich habe **ihn** gern.
	Ich habe Julia gern.	Ich habe **sie** gern.
	Ich habe Michael und Julia gern.	Ich habe **sie** gern.
	Ich habe das Mädchen gern.	Ich habe **es** gern.

Since German nouns have gender in their singular form, the direct object pronouns must also show gender.

referring to things:	Ich habe den Pulli gern.	Ich habe **ihn** gern.
	Ich habe die Jacke gern.	Ich habe **sie** gern.
	Ich habe das Hemd gern.	Ich habe **es** gern.
	Ich habe die Schuhe gern. (plural)	Ich habe **sie** gern.

Comparing the German sentences with the English sentences above, what are the German words for the English pronoun *it?*

In all the sentences above, the pronouns as well as the nouns and noun phrases to which they refer are the direct object of the verb **haben** and are in the **accusative case**.

B. Underline the word or words to which the object pronoun in the following statements can refer.

1. Ich finde sie echt schick.	Hemd	Stiefel	Pulli	Bluse
2. Nein, ich kaufe ihn nicht.	Jeans	Rock	T-Shirt	Pulli
3. Ich ziehe es so gern an.	Kleid	Shorts	Jacke	Hemd
4. Ich finde sie nicht teuer.	Stiefel	Gürtel	Hose	Rock
5. Wir brauchen ihn nicht.	Gürtel	Jacke	Klamotten	T-Shirt
6. Er zieht es nicht gern an.	Jacke	Hemd	T-Shirt	Pulli
7. Ich möchte ihn in Blau.	Jeans	Jacke	Hemd	Pulli
8. Sie probiert sie mal an.	Jacke	Gürtel	Pulli	Hemd
9. Haben Sie es auch in Rot?	Jacke	Hemd	Schuhe	Bluse
10. Ich finde ihn zu eng.	Hose	Gürtel	Schuhe	Hemd

C. Fill in each blank with the correct object pronoun.

1. Wie findest du die Hose? Ich finde ___sie___ mega-toll!
2. Wie findest du Ann? Ich finde ______ okay.
3. Wie findet ihr den Pullover? Wir finden ______ sehr schick.
4. Wie findet ihr mein T-Shirt? Wir finden ______ scheußlich!
5. Wie findet Mark seine Freundin? Er findet ______ sehr nett.
6. Wie findet Susan ihre Großeltern? Sie findet ______ lieb und nett.
7. Wie findest du das Bett? Ich finde ______ sehr hart.
8. Wie findet ihr die Turnschuhe? Wir finden ______ zu teuer.
9. Wie findest du den Gürtel? Ich finde ______ zu lang.
10. Wie findet ihr eueren Lehrer? Wir finden ______ sehr nett.

D. In your own words, summarize what you know about German object pronouns.

____

____

____

SEPARABLE-PREFIX VERBS

Compare There are no **separable-prefix verbs** in English. However, look at the following verbs and think of all the different meanings of *to put on, to put up, to put down, to put upon.*

Look at the following example and compare it to the first German example below.

to put **on** I am putting a T-shirt **on**. What are you putting **on**?

In German there are special verbs with prefixes that affect the meaning of the verb. For example, the verb **ziehen** by itself means *to pull,* **an**ziehen means *to put on, wear,* and **aus**ziehen means *to take off (clothes)* or *to move out.* Such verbs are called **separable-prefix verbs** because the prefix is most often separated from the verb and put at the end of the sentence.

anziehen	Ich ziehe ein T-Shirt **an**. Was ziehst du **an**?
anprobieren	Ich probiere mal die Jacke **an**.
aussehen	Du siehst einfach toll **aus**!

A. Underline all verbs and circle all separable prefixes (if any).

1. Der Pulli sieht wirklich gut aus.
2. Ich finde den Pulli wirklich stark!
3. Warum probierst du die Hose nicht an?
4. Ich ziehe den Jogging-Anzug zur Fete an.
5. Sieht mein T-Shirt nicht fesch aus?
6. Ich kaufe die Bluse nicht.
7. Die Schuhe sehen toll aus, aber sie sind zu teuer.
8. Simone nimmt die Hose nicht.
9. Probierst du das Kleid oder den Rock an?
10. Die Stiefel sehen toll aus, nicht?

B. Use the following separable-prefix verbs correctly in each sentence.

1. (anziehen) Ich ___ziehe___ zur Fete ein T-Shirt ___an___ .
2. (aussehen) Du ________ wirklich sehr gut ________ .
3. (anprobieren) Ralph ________ jetzt die Hose ________ .
4. (anziehen) Was ________ du denn zur Fete ________ ?
5. (aussehen) Wie ________ ihr denn schon wieder ________ ?
6. (anprobieren) Wer ________ jetzt die Turnschuhe ________ ?
7. (anprobieren) Wir ________ jetzt die Turnschuhe ________ .
8. (anziehen) Gerd und Uwe ________ immer Jeans und T-Shirts ________ .
9. (aussehen) Mensch, die Jacke ________ aber toll ________ ! Ganz fesch!
10. (aussehen) Die Hose da ________ doch furchtbar ________ !

C. What can you say about separable-prefix verbs in your own words?

____

____

____

KAPITEL 5

KAPITEL 6

WORD ORDER: EXPRESSIONS OF TIME AND PLACE

Pupil's Edition, p. 167

In English As a rule, **expressions of place** come before **expressions of time**.

I'm going to school at 8 o'clock.
We're going to the movies tonight.
Who wants to go to the concert on the weekend?

A. Underline all expressions of time and circle all expressions of place.

1. We want to go to the disco at night.
2. I want to go to the mall in the morning.
3. Who wants to go to the pool at 10 o'clock?
4. Susan wants to go to the tennis court early in the morning.
5. Why do you want to go to Berlin in the winter?
6. We want to go to the mountains in the fall.
7. My parents want to fly to Germany in October.
8. But who does not want to go to the Oktoberfest in the fall?
9. Are you going to the café after school?
10. I would like to be at the airport by noon.

In German Look at these German sentences and note the placement of time expressions.

	TIME	PLACE
Ich gehe	um acht Uhr	zur Schule.
Wir gehen	heute Abend	ins Kino.
Wer fährt	morgen	nach Wedel?

In German sentences **time expressions** come first, followed by **expressions of place**.

B. Underline all expressions of time and circle all expressions of place.

1. Wir wollen nach der Schule in die Stadt gehen.
2. Wollt ihr am Abend ins Konzert gehen?
3. Der Johannes möchte am Nachmittag in ein Café gehen.

4. Ich will um vier Uhr ins Kino gehen.
5. Willst du jetzt ins Schwimmbad gehen?
6. Ich möchte nach der Mathestunde nach Hause gehen.
7. Meine Eltern fliegen im Winter nach Spanien.
8. Prima! Wer möchte nicht im Dezember nach Florida fliegen?
9. Brenna und Erik wollen am Wochenende ins Schwimmbad gehen.
10. Gregor, willst du um halb vier ins Café gehen?

C. Rewrite the following sentences, inserting the time expressions given in parentheses in the correct position.

1. (um Viertel nach neun) Ich möchte in die Stadt fahren.

   Ich möchte um Viertel nach neun in die Stadt fahren.

2. (nach der Schule) Wir wollen Fußball spielen.

3. (danach) Der Mike möchte ins Schwimmbad gehen.

4. (am Abend) Wollt ihr ins Kino gehen?

5. (jetzt) Meine Mutter möchte ins Einkaufszentrum fahren.

6. (um Viertel vor vier) Die Jungen wollen ins Café Freizeit gehen.

7. (heute) Wollt ihr ins Rockkonzert gehen?

8. (nach der Biostunde) Ich möchte nach Hause gehen.

9. (am Wochenende) Hans und Maria wollen in die Disko gehen.

10. (Freitag) Wir wollen nach Berlin fahren.

D. How would you summarize what you have learned about the positon of time expressions and expressions of place?

KAPITEL 7

SEPARABLE-PREFIX VERBS AND MODALS

Pupil's Edition, p. 196

In German Earlier you were introduced to a sentence and a question such as:

Ich ziehe ein T-Shirt **an**. Was ziehst du **an**?

The infinitive of this separable-prefix verb is **an**ziehen, and the verb is separated in the present tense, with the prefix used at the end of the sentence.

Modal verbs can be used with an infinitive at the end of the sentence. When the infinitive (main verb) is a separable-prefix verb, it remains intact.

Was **möchtest** du **an**ziehen? – Ich **möchte** einen Pulli **an**ziehen.
Was **will** Markus **auf**räumen? – Er **will** die Garage **auf**räumen.

A. Complete each of the following sentences by filling in the infinitive of the separable-prefix verb.

1. Was probierst du an? – Ich will die Jacke **anprobieren** .
2. Was räumt der Flori ab? – Er muss den Tisch ________________ .
3. Wie siehst du denn aus? – Ich möchte wie ein Filmstar ________________ .
4. Wann räumst du dein Zimmer auf? – Ich will es heute Abend ________________ .
5. Kommst du heute mit? – Du, ich möchte heute nicht ________________ .
6. Was ziehe ich nur an? – Willst du nicht deine Jeans ________________ ?
7. Probiert Kurt die Turnschuhe an? – Nein, er will die Stiefel ________________ .
8. Probierst du die Hose oder die Jacke an? – Ich möchte die Hose ________________ .
9. Kommt Katrin mit ins Kino? – Ja, sie möchte ins Kino ________________ .
10. Wer räumt den Tisch ab? – Die Sabine muss den Tisch ________________ .

B. Rewrite each of the following sentences using the modal verb in parentheses.

1. (können) Ich probiere die Jacke nicht an.
   Ich kann die Jacke nicht anprobieren.
2. (müssen) Du ziehst die Stiefel an.
3. (können) Wer räumt den Tisch ab?
4. (müssen) Claudia räumt die Klamotten auf.
5. (können) Wer kommt mit?
6. (müssen) Ich probiere zuerst die Schuhe an.
7. (wollen) Marga sieht gut aus.
8. (möchten) Jens und Lars ziehen Jeans an.
9. (wollen) Max räumt den Tisch nicht ab.
10. (möchten) Anna probiert die Schuhe an.

C. How would you describe what you have learned about sentences in which a modal verb and a separable-prefix verb are used together in your own words?

OBJECT PRONOUNS: SECOND PERSON

Pupil's Edition, p. 200

In English The underlined pronouns are subjects, the boldfaced pronouns are object pronouns. They are the object of the verb.

Do you like **me**? Yes, I like **you**.
Hannah and Ken, we like **you**. Really? Do you like **us**?

A. Underline the subject pronouns and circle the object pronouns.

1. We can see (you) in the afternoon.
2. Will you call us in the afternoon?
3. He might ask you out.
4. I find you very interesting.
5. Would you see me after class?
6. She needs her to set the table.
7. We'll visit her on the weekend.
8. Do you see him in the library?

Compare The following list compares English subject and object pronouns to German **subject** and **object pronouns**. The German first- and second-person pronouns are in boldface.

		Subject	Object	Subject: Nominative	Object: Accusative
1st person, sing.		I	me	ich	**mich**
2nd person, sing.		you	you	du	**dich**
3rd person, sing.	m.	he	him	er	ihn
	f.	she	her	sie	sie
	n.	it	it	es	es
1st person, pl.		we	us	wir	**uns**
2nd person, pl.		you	you	ihr	**euch**
3rd person, pl.		they	them	sie	sie
formal address		(none)	(none)	Sie	**Sie**

KAPITEL 7

B. Circle the direct object pronouns in the following sentences.

1. Ich besuche (dich) nach der Schule.
2. Wer möchte uns heute besuchen?
3. Ich möchte Sie etwas fragen, Herr Müller.
4. Warum brauchst du mich heute?
5. Wann wollt ihr uns einmal besuchen?
6. Ich finde dich einfach toll!
7. Ich besuche Sie heute nach der Schule.
8. Wir möchten euch gern etwas fragen.

C. Fill in each blank with the correct form of the direct object pronoun.

1. Mark, wir möchten ___dich___ nach der Schule besuchen.
2. Toll! Ihr möchtet ________ nach der Schule besuchen.
3. Wir haben tolle Musik. Wann wollt ihr ________ besuchen?
4. Hallo, Frau Moser! Ich bin's. Hören Sie ________ ?
5. Wo können wir ________ finden, Ahmet?
6. Hallo, ihr beiden. Ihr könnt ________ nach der Schule besuchen.
7. Kann ich ________ etwas fragen, Herr Schröder?
8. Hannes und Frieda, kann ich ________ etwas fragen?

D. How would you summarize what you have learned about first- and second-person object pronouns?

____

____

____

KAPITEL 8

COMMAND FORMS: THE DU-COMMAND AND THE IHR-COMMAND

Pupil's Edition, p. 224

In English **Command forms** are used to tell someone else what to do. The *you* command is used to give an order to one person or several persons. In English, we use the unconjugated verb form (the dictionary verb form) to give a command.

Go home. Come along. Buy apples and grapes.

Notice that when giving orders or instructions, the pronoun *you* is not used. The *you* is understood.

You go home. (present tense) Go home. (command form)

A. Underline the present-tense verb forms and circle the command forms.

1. I eat bread every day. (Eat) bread every day!
2. We watch TV and turn it off at 9 o'clock. Watch TV and turn it off at 9 o'clock.
3. Go home to read the newpaper. I go home to read the newspaper.
4. We'll take the money. Take the money.
5. Sort the garbage for your mother. I'll sort the garbage for your mother.
6. You tell good stories. Tell me when you're done.
7. Be at school at 7:30. No, you should be there at 7:20.
8. Clear the table today. We'll clear the table tomorrow.

KAPITEL 8

In German The **command forms** work like English in that the pronoun is understood: no **du** or **ihr** is used in the command itself. The **du**-command uses the verb stem (or the **du**-form of the verb without the ending **-st**). The **ihr**-command uses the **ihr**-form of the verb.

Notice that irregular verbs that add the umlaut **ä** in the **du**-form do not have the umlaut in the command form.

giving a command or an instruction to one person

statement	Du **geh**st jetzt nach Hause.	command	**Geh** jetzt nach Hause!
statement	Du **komm**st mit.	command	**Komm** mit!
question	**Nimm**st du eine Cola?	command	**Nimm** eine Cola!
question	**Fähr**st du nach Hause?	command	**Fahr** nach Hause!

giving a command or an instruction to more than one person

statement	Ihr **geht** jetzt ins Kino.	command	**Geht** jetzt ins Kino!
statement	Ihr **kommt** doch mit.	command	**Kommt** doch mit!

Strong commands require an exclamation point, whereas mild commands or instructions don't.

B. Underline the present-tense verb forms (if any) and circle the command forms in these German sentences.

1. Kauf doch das Brot beim Bäcker, und du gehst jetzt zuerst zum Supermarkt, ja?
2. Räumt das Zimmer auf, und ihr sortiert den Müll!
3. Besuch zuerst die Oma, und geht dann zusammen einkaufen!
4. Macht zuerst die Hausaufgaben und schaut danach Fernsehen!
5. Rolf, frag den Biolehrer, und ihr fragt den Deutschlehrer nach der Pause!
6. Geh ins Kino oder geh den Opa besuchen!

C. Are the command forms singular or plural? Underline the singular commands and circle the plural commands.

1. Kauf die Wurst lieber beim Metzger und holt die Milch im Supermarkt!
2. Wiegt das Gemüse und zahlt nicht zu viel für das Obst!
3. Mach das Bett und räumt zusammen das Zimmer auf.
4. Sortiert zuerst den Müll und fahrt danach zusammen in die Stadt.
5. Kommt doch mit zum Bäcker, aber du, Holger, zieh zuerst dein Hemd an!
6. Bestell doch eine Pizza und trink eine Limo dazu.

KAPITEL 8

D. Fill in each blank with the correct command form of the verb given in parentheses.

1. (holen) Flori, **hol** das Brot lieber beim Bäcker.
2. (kaufen) Flori und Mara, ____________ das Gemüse im Supermarkt.
3. (vergessen) Flori und Mara, ____________ das Geld nicht.
4. (aufräumen) Claudi, ____________ endlich mal dein Zimmer ____________ !
5. (sortieren) Markus und Flori, ____________ bitte jetzt den Müll.
6. (mähen) Markus, ____________ den Rasen erst am Wochenende.
7. (machen) Kinder, ____________ jetzt endlich mal eure Hausaufgaben!

E. How would you summarize what you know about the German **du**-command and **ihr**- command?

____

____

____

SENTENCES AND CLAUSES

In English A **sentence** is a word or group of words that contains at least a subject and a verb and expresses a complete thought.

I buy the bread at the baker's.

A **complex sentence** consists of a **main clause** and a **subordinate clause**. The **main clause** can stand on its own. A **subordinate clause** cannot stand alone as a complete sentence. It depends on the main clause for its full meaning, and it is subordinate to the main clause.

I buy the bread at the baker's because it is always fresh there.

The clause "because it is always fresh there" is not a complete sentence, and it depends on the main clause "I buy the bread at the baker's."

A. Underline the main clauses and circle the subordinate clauses.

1. We get our groceries at the supermarket because they are cheaper there.
2. I like to eat vegetables because they are good for me.
3. My father listens to classical music because he likes it better than anything else.
4. I can't play soccer today because I have no time.
5. Jenna must do her homework more diligently because she needs better grades.
6. Mom must clean the house because my grandparents are coming to see us.
7. Traffic is heavy because it is 5:00.
8. Because flooding at the lake is ongoing, we can't vacation there this year.

KAPITEL 8

Clauses introduced by Conjunctions (denn and weil)

Compare A **conjunction** is a word that joins together words, word groups, sentences, or clauses; in English, words such as *and, but, because, as.*

I can't go to the movies *because* I have no time.

In German Clauses can be introduced by **conjunctions** such as **denn** and **weil**. Both **denn** and **weil** mean *because*. **Denn** requires the conjugated verb to be in regular position within the clause; **weil** requires the conjugated verb to be at the end of the clause.

Sentence: Ich kann nicht ins Kino gehen.
Complex sentence: Ich kann nicht ins Kino gehen, **weil** ich keine Zeit **habe**.
Ich kann nicht ins Kino gehen, **denn** ich **habe** keine Zeit.
Ich kann nicht ins Kino gehen, **weil** ich zu Hause helfen **muss**.
Ich kann nicht ins Kino gehen, **denn** ich **muss** zu Hause helfen.

As in English, the German clauses introduced by the conjunctions **weil** and **denn** cannot stand alone, but depend on the main clause **Ich kann nicht ins Kino gehen** for their meaning. Notice that a comma is required between the two clauses.

B. Underline the main clauses and circle the conjunctions.

1. Ich gehe nicht schwimmen, weil ich meine Hausaufgaben machen muss.
2. Julia kann den Pulli nicht kaufen, denn sie hat kein Geld.
3. Wir waren nicht beim Bäcker, weil wir noch Brot zu Hause haben.
4. Ein deutsches Pfund wiegt mehr, weil es 500 Gramm hat.
5. Ich möchte noch ein Ei, denn ich habe Hunger.
6. Wir gehen nicht ins Kino, weil wir erst letzte Woche im Kino waren.
7. Du musst einkaufen gehen, denn du brauchst neue Klamotten.
8. Die Mutti kann heute nicht zum Supermarkt fahren, weil sie keine Zeit hat.

C. Underline the clauses beginning with a conjunction, then circle the conjugated verb in that clause.

1. Ich gehe zum Metzger, weil ich Fleisch und Wurst kaufen muss.
2. Wir können heute nicht Tennis spielen, denn wir haben keine Zeit.
3. Sean muss zu Hause helfen, weil seine Schwester etwas anderes machen muss.
4. Ich hab das Brot beim Bäcker gekauft, denn es ist dort immer frisch.
5. Ich kann dir nicht helfen, weil ich zu Hause so viel zu tun habe.
6. Ihr müsst zu Hause bleiben, weil ihr den Müll noch nicht sortiert habt.
7. Wir können dich heute Abend nicht anrufen, denn wir sind alle bei den Großeltern.
8. Ich soll heute ins Kino gehen, weil es dort einen guten Film gibt.

D. How would you summarize what you have learned about German clauses and the position of the conjugated verb in such clauses?

____

____

____

KAPITEL 9

FORMAL SIE-COMMAND

Pupil's Edition, p. 255

In German German has three different forms of address in the second person:

Gehst **du** nach Hause, Michael?
Geht **ihr** nach Hause, Michael und Mark?
Gehen **Sie** nach Hause, Frau Weigel?

Therefore, German also has three command forms.

addressing one friend:	**Geh** nach Hause, Michael!
addressing two or more friends:	**Geht** nach Hause, Michael und Mark!

In the formal command, the **Sie**-command, you use the third-person plural verb form (the infinitive form) in first position, followed by the pronoun **Sie**.

singular	**Gehen Sie** nach Hause, Frau Weigel!
plural	**Gehen Sie** nach Hause, Herr und Frau Müller!

A. Are the following commands **du**-, **ihr**-, or **Sie**-commands? Check the appropriate column.

	du	ihr	Sie
1. Fahr immer geradeaus!	✓		
2. Fahren Sie nach links!			
3. Fahrt bis zur Ampel!			
4. Schauen Sie mal auf den Stadtplan!			
5. Schau mal auf die Stadtkarte.			
6. Schaut mal auf die Straßenkarte!			
7. Komm sofort nach Hause!			
8. Trinken Sie doch mal ein Glas Milch!			
9. Wartet beim Bäcker!			
10. Geh nicht so schnell!			

B. Rewrite these **du**-commands as **Sie**-commands.

1. Geh doch nach Hause. **Gehen Sie doch nach Hause.**
2. Fahr bis zur Ampel. ______
3. Trink mal ein Mineralwasser. ______
4. Sortier den Müll. ______
5. Kauf das Brot beim Bäcker. ______
6. Frag mal die Schüler. ______
7. Fahr bitte nicht so schnell. ______
8. Warte auf mich am Rathaus. ______
9. Komm doch mit! ______
10. Füttre bitte die Katze für mich. ______

C. Rewrite the sentences in parentheses as **Sie**-commands. To be polite, use the word **bitte** in the commands.

1. (Er soll das Wort an die Tafel schreiben.)

   Schreiben Sie bitte das Wort an die Tafel.
2. (Sie soll das Wort buchstabieren.)

   ______
3. (Er soll langsam sprechen.)

   ______
4. (Sie soll den Test morgen geben.)

   ______
5. (Er soll die Eltern heute Abend anrufen.)

   ______
6. (Sie soll im Schulhof warten.)

   ______

D. How would you summarize what you have learned about **Sie**-commands?

______

______

THERE IS, THERE ARE

Compare In English the phrase **there is** refers to one thing, **there are** to more than one thing.

> There is a supermarket nearby.
> There are two bakeries on this street.

In German the phrase **es gibt** can refer to singular or plural objects. The verb form never changes.

> **Es gibt** einen Supermarkt in der Nähe.
> **Es gibt** zwei Bäckereien in dieser Straße.
> Was **gibt es** in der Imbissstube?

In questions, the verb is in first position, or in second position when the question begins with an interrogative.

> **Gibt es** hier eine gute Bäckerei?
> Wo **gibt es** hier ein nettes Café?

A. Write either *there is* or *there are* in the space provided.

1. ___**There is**___ a nice museum downtown.
2. ____________________ many museums in Munich.
3. ____________________ also various outdoor markets.
4. But ____________________ usually only one town hall.
5. ____________________ lots of visitors in town.
6. And ____________________ only one good tourist office.
7. ____________________ several good cafés.
8. ____________________ a restaurant guide that lists other places to eat.
9. ____________________ no reason to be bored in Munich.
10. ____________________ too many interesting things to see and do.

B. Write the equivalent form of *there is* or *there are* in the space provided.

1. ______**Es gibt**______ Leberkäs zum Essen.
2. Ich esse nicht viel Leberkäs, weil ____________________ auch Brezeln dazu ____________________ .
3. Was ____________________ zu trinken?
4. ____________________ Saft, Cola und Mineralwasser.
5. ____________________ heute Hähnchen vom Grill und Gyros mit Salat.
6. Was ____________________ alles in der Imbissstube am Rathaus?
7. In der Imbissstube ____________________ Weißwurst, Leberkäs und Gyros.
8. ____________________ auch ein Café am Marienplatz?
9. Ja, im Café ____________________ Eis und Kuchen.
10. München ist prima, denn ____________________ immer viel zu tun.

C. How would you summarize what you have learned about the phrase **es gibt** in your own words?

____

____

NEGATION: NICHT AND KEIN

Pupil's Edition, p. 259

In English A **negation** expresses the absence of something actual, true, or real. Words and phrases used to negate sentences are *not, not a,* and *no,* depending on whether the element being negated is a noun, a verb, or an adjective.

> Holger lives on Copernicus Street.
> negation of a verb: Holger does not live on Copernicus Street.
>
> The cat is white.
> negation of an adjective: The cat is not white.
>
> I have time. / That is an apple.
> negation of a verb: I do not have time. / That is not an apple.
> negation of a noun: I have no time. / That is no apple!

What parts of speech are negated by *not* or *not a?* What part of speech is negated by *no?* Notice that when negating sentences containing a noun phrase, you have a choice between negating the noun phrase or negating the verb.

A. Underline the words that negate the statements.

1. I don't eat the cake because I'm not hungry.
2. I have no money, and I cannot go to Berlin.
3. I cannot play tennis because I have no time.
4. I don't know where the station is. I have no idea.
5. We are not vegetarians, but we eat no meat.
6. I have no car, and I cannot come to see you.

B. Write down the phrases that use the word "no" to make them negative. What part of speech always follows "no"?

____

In German You have already been using **nicht** to make negative statements with verbs and adjectives.

> Der Holger wohnt **nicht** in der Kopernikusstraße.
> Die Katze ist **nicht** weiß.

Above, you learned that when negating English sentences containing noun phrases, you may either negate the noun phrase or the verb (*That's no excuse* vs. *That's not an excuse.*). In German, it is customary to negate the noun phrase, not the verb. The word used to negate the noun phrase (the equivalent of no) is **kein**.

Ich habe Zeit.	*I have time.*
Ich habe **keine** Zeit.	*I do not have time. (I have no time.)*
Das ist ein Apfel.	*That is an apple.*
Das ist **kein** Apfel.	*That is not an apple. (That is no apple.)*

Kein is an **ein**-word. It has the same endings as all the other **ein**-words (**ein, mein, dein**, etc.) and is a part of the noun phrase.

C. Underline the words that negate the statements.

1. Ich esse den Kuchen nicht, weil ich keinen Hunger habe.
2. Ich habe kein Geld und kann nicht nach Berlin fahren.
3. Ich kann nicht Tennis spielen, weil ich keine Zeit habe.
4. Ich weiß nicht, wo der Bahnhof ist. Ich habe keine Ahnung.
5. Ich kann den Saft nicht trinken, weil ich keinen Durst habe.
6. Wir haben kein Brot, weil ich nicht einkaufen war.
7. Wir können nicht in die Disko gehen, weil wir kein Geld haben.
8. Wir essen keine Wurst mehr, weil wir nicht wissen, was in der Wurst ist.

D. Would you use **nicht** or **kein** to negate these sentences?

	nicht	**kein**
1. Ich kann gut Gitarre spielen.	✓	
2. Wir haben Geld.		
3. Wir haben auch Zeit.		
4. Mein Freund weiß, wo der Marktplatz ist.		
5. Hast du eine Ahnung, wo die Post ist?		
6. Ich habe Leberkäs gekauft.		
7. Ich esse Weißwurst so gern.		

E. Negate the following sentences.

1. Ich weiß, wo der Marktplatz ist. **Ich weiß nicht, wo der Marktplatz ist.**
2. Ich habe jetzt Zeit. ______________________
3. Ich esse, weil ich Hunger habe. ______________________
4. Ich esse Wurst, weil ich sie mag. ______________________
5. Ich weiß, warum du Spinat isst! ______________________
6. Sag, warum du Zeit hast! ______________________
7. Wir haben einen Garten. ______________________
8. Ich warte am Marktplatz. ______________________

F. How would you summarize what you have learned about negations and the words used to make sentences negative?

____

____

KAPITEL 11

INDIRECT OBJECTS

Pupil's Edition, p. 319

In English An **indirect object** is a noun, a pronoun, or a noun phrase that can appear in sentences containing direct objects. Indirect objects tell *to whom* or *to what,* or *for whom* or *for what,* the action of the verb is done. If a sentence has an indirect object, it always has a direct object. The indirect objects are underlined.

Sandra buys Martin a T-shirt.	*For whom* does Sandra buy the T-shirt?
She buys him a T-shirt.	*For whom* does she buy the T-shirt?
Martin gives his grandma flowers.	*To whom* does Martin give flowers?
Martin gives her the flowers.	*To whom* does Martin give the flowers?

Notice that the direct object is usually a thing, while the indirect object is usually a person.

A. Underline the direct objects and circle the indirect objects.

1. Andreas gives (Martin) a glass of juice.
2. Nicole buys him a beautiful birthday cake.
3. Will you tell me a story?
4. Pass your father a roll.
5. I sent him the bill last week.
6. You should offer the old lady your seat.
7. My mother gave me the flu.
8. Julia presented the winner a trophy.
9. The mechanic gave my car a tune-up.
10. Could you please bring me a book?

In German The **indirect object** is signalled by the **dative case**. The usual word order is indirect object first, followed by the direct object.

	Indirect Object	Direct Object
Sandra kauft	**dem Martin**	ein T-Shirt.

In sentences where the indirect object is emphasized, the indirect object can be used in first position.

Indirect Object		Direct Object
Dem Martin	kauft Sandra	ein T-Shirt.

In the following examples the indirect objects are **boldfaced** and the direct objects are underlined.

Sandra kauft **Martin** ein T-Shirt.
Martin gibt **seiner Oma** Blumen.
Wem gibt Martin die Blumen?

Sie kauft **ihm** ein T-Shirt.
Seiner Oma gibt Martin Blumen.
Seinem Opa.

B. Underline all direct objects and circle all indirect objects in these German sentences.

1. Ich habe meiner Mutti Blumen gekauft.
2. Meinem Vati habe ich Pralinen gekauft, und ich habe ihm auch Blumen geschenkt.
3. Meinen Freunden kaufe ich CDs zum Geburtstag.
4. Wir kaufen den Eltern ein Handy, und wir geben ihnen auch zwei Telefonkarten.
5. Dem Martin gebe ich Pralinen, und ich schenke ihm auch einen Kalender.
6. Meiner Freundin schenke ich ein Video, und ich gebe ihr auch ein Buch.

C. Rewrite each of the following sentences, beginning each one with the indirect object.

1. Wir schenken unseren Eltern eine CD.

   Unseren Eltern schenken wir eine CD.

2. Ich schenke meinem Bruder ein Buch.

   ____

3. Ich schenke meiner Schwester ein Handy.

   ____

4. Wir schenken dem Vati ein Sachbuch.

   ____

5. Ich schenke der Mutti eine Telefonkarte.

   ____

6. Wir schenken den Jungen Klamotten.

   ____

7. Alex schenkt den Großeltern ein Video.

   ____

8. Ich kaufe meiner Freundin Pralinen.

   ____

9. Ich gebe meiner Tante einen Blumenstrauß.

   ____

10. Wir schenken dem Lehrer einen Kuli.

   ____

D. How would you summarize what you have learned about indirect objects in your own words?

____

KAPITEL 12

TO KNOW (SUMMARY)

Pupil's Edition, p. 340

Compare For the English verb *to know,* three different German verbs can be used, depending on the precise meaning.

For "to know a fact or information," use **wissen**.

> **Wissen Sie**, wie spät es ist?
> **Wisst ihr**, wo das Rathaus ist?

For "to know a person, to be acquainted with," use **kennen**.

> **Kennst du** Udo Lindenberg?
> **Kennen Sie** das Buch *Harry Potter und der Feuerkelch* von J. K. Rowling?

For "to know a language or skill," use **können**.

> **Kannst du** gut Deutsch?
> Nein, aber ich **kann** Karate.

A. Write a correct form of **wissen**, **kennen**, or **können** in the space provided.

1. Ich **kenne** deinen Deutschlehrer nicht.
2. Ich glaube, dein Mathelehrer ________________ auch Spanisch.
3. Ich ________________ nicht, wo dein Biolehrer wohnt.
4. Wir ________________ aber nicht, wohin wir den Müll geben sollen.
5. Wer ________________ den Film „Patriot"?
6. Ich ________________ nicht, ob (*whether*) mein Bruder den Film ________________ .
7. Wir ________________ nicht, ob sein Vater Klavier spielen ________________ .
8. Wer ________________ den deutschen Kanzler, und wer ________________ , wie er heißt?
9. Ich ________________ , dass unser Lehrer auch Spanisch ________________ .
10. Wir ________________ deinen Bruder nicht, aber wir ________________ , dass er Karate ________________ .

B. How would you summarize what you have learned about the three ways of expressing "to know" in German?

____

____

____

MOOD AND MODAL VERBS (SUMMARY) *Pupil's Edition, p. 348*

Compare When talking about **mood** we refer to verbs, such as the modals, that express functions, such as *ability, desire, possibility,* and so on.

dürfen, *may, to be allowed to,* expresses the function of asking for or granting permission

Darf ich heute ins Kino gehen?

können, *can, to be able to,* expresses the function of being able to do something, or knowing a skill

Kannst du bitte für mich die Fenster putzen? Kannst du Deutsch?

wollen, *to want to,* expresses the function of wish, desire, or intention

Was wollt ihr heute machen? Wir wollen Fußball spielen.

sollen, *should, to be supposed to,* expresses the function of obligation

Wo sollen wir das Brot kaufen? Sollen wir das Obst beim Gemüsehändler kaufen?

müssen, *must, to have to,* expresses the function of necessity or compulsion

Ich muss heute meine Hausaufgaben machen.

möchte-forms, *would like (to),* express the function of wish or desire

Möchtest du mit mir in eine Disko gehen?

A. Write sentences using what you know about the various meanings of the modals.

(den Müll sortieren)

1. We can sort the garbage. **Wir können den Müll sortieren.**
2. We want to sort the garbage. ______
3. We're supposed to sort the garbage. ______
4. We would like to sort the garbage. ______
5. We must sort the garbage. ______
6. We are allowed to sort the garbage today. ______

B. Write sentences using what you know about the various functions expressed by the modals.

(den Film nicht sehen)

1. I don't want to see the movie. ______
2. I would not like to see the movie. ______
3. I must not see the movie. ______
4. I'm not supposed to see the movie. ______
5. I cannot see the movie. ______
6. We are not allowed to see the movie. ______

MODAL VERBS (A SUMMARY)

Pupil's Edition, p. 348

Compare Both English and German have a set of helping verbs, often referred to as **modal verbs** (or modal auxiliaries) that are used with other verbs to express mood or possibility. The modal verbs are conjugated for person and number, and they can be used with an unconjugated verb. Here are the modal verbs that you have learned:

MODALS	EXAMPLES
können	Ich kann gehen.
müssen	Er muss gehen.
sollen	Sie soll gehen.
wollen	Wir wollen gehen.
möchte-forms	Sie möchten gehen.

The German modals have these forms in the present tense, using **können** as an example:

	SINGULAR			PLURAL	
Ich	kann	nichts essen.	Wir	könn**en**	nichts essen.
Du	kann**st**	nichts essen.	Ihr	könn**t**	nichts essen.
Er, sie, es	kann	nichts essen.	Sie	könn**en**	nichts essen.

What do you notice about the different verb forms?

A. Circle both the modal verb and the infinitive in the following sentences.

1. Wir (möchten) heute mal die Stadt (besichtigen).
2. Wollt ihr nicht lieber in den Zoo gehen?
3. Ich soll zu Hause bleiben. Ich muss meinen Eltern helfen.
4. Warum kannst du das nicht morgen tun?
5. Ich muss morgen die Garage aufräumen.
6. Willst du denn überhaupt nicht mehr mit uns weggehen?
7. Warum wollt ihr nicht mit uns ins Kino gehen?
8. Ich muss heute meine Hausaufgaben machen.

B. Fill in each blank with the correct form of the modal verb given in parentheses.

1. (können) Ich **kann** heute nicht ins Kino gehen.
2. (wollen) Du ______________ diesen Film nicht sehen?
3. (müssen) Ihr ______________ zuerst die Hausaufgaben machen.
4. (sollen) Wo ______________ wir die Kinokarten kaufen?
5. (wollen) Martin ______________ lieber in ein Konzert gehen.
6. (möchte-form) Was ______________ du denn am liebsten sehen?

7. (können) Ihr ______________________ das wirklich nicht wissen.

8. (sollen) Was ______________________ ihr im Supermarkt kaufen?

C. Fill in each blank with the correct form of the verb.

1. dürfen / gehen ______Dürfen______ Sie heute Abend auf die Fete ______gehen______ ?
2. können / kaufen Ja, aber ich ________________ kein Geschenk ________________ .
3. wollen / anrufen Zuerst ________________ ich meine Freundin ________________ .
4. möchte / sagen Was ________________ du ihr denn ________________ ?
5. wollen / einladen Ich ________________ sie zur Fete ________________ .
6. müssen / machen Warum ________________ ihr die Party am Montag ________________?

D. How would you summarize what you know about the forms of modal verbs and how they are used in a sentence?

____

____

KAPITEL 12

Grammar Tutor Activities
Komm mit!
German 2

KAPITEL 1 (WIEDERHOLUNG)

VERBS, PRESENT TENSE (REVIEW)

Pupil's Edition, pp. 11, 12

In English The **present tense** is used to indicate **present time**. In English there are three present-tense verb forms to indicate present time.

We **help** around the house on the weekend. (regular)
I **am helping** you right now. (progressive)
She **does help** me a lot. (emphatic)

A. Underline the present-tense verb forms in these English sentences.

1. You are not playing soccer on the weekend?
2. Yes, I do play soccer on the weekend.
3. Where are you spending your vacation?
4. We are going to Austria, to the mountains.
5. My grandparents live in Salzburg.
6. We are visiting them next summer.
7. My sister plays chess very well.
8. Sometimes I play with her, and then I lose.

In German There is **one present-tense** form to indicate **present time**. There is no progressive or emphatic present tense.

Wir **helfen** am Wochenende zu Hause.
Ich **helfe** dir jetzt.
Sie **hilft** mir viel.
Ich **bin** am Sonntag in Bayern.
Wir **haben** am Wochenende keine Zeit.

German verbs have endings in the present tense: **-e, -st, -t, -en, -et,** depending on who is performing the action of the verb. Some verbs have irregular forms in the second and third persons, such as **lesen, nehmen, fahren**. The verbs **haben** and **sein** also have irregular forms.

Ich mäh**e** den Rasen.
Du gi**bst** mir deine CD, ja?
Wann spiel**t** Tara Tennis?
Wir sortier**en** den Müll.
Ihr wart**et** doch auf den Lehrer.
Wo spiel**en** die Schüler? Und wo spiel**en** Sie, Herr Meier?

B. Fill in each blank with the correct verb ending.

1. Wohin geh__st__ du nach der Schule?
2. Ich geh_____ mit meiner Freundin ins Kino.
3. Was mach____ ihr nach dem Kino?
4. Wir kauf____ ein Geschenk für die Party.
5. Komm____ die Tina auch zur Party?
6. Tina und Randy komm____ zur Party.
7. Sag, wie find____ du Ricks Partys?
8. Ich find____ sie blöd und langweilig.

KAPITEL 1

C. Fill in each blank with the correct form of the verb in parentheses.

1. (kommen) Wann **kommst** du heute Abend nach Hause?
2. (glauben) Ich ______________ mit dem Bus um 22 Uhr.
3. (probieren) Warum ______________ ihr nicht mal den Leberkäs?
4. (haben) Also, ich ______________ keinen Hunger mehr.
5. (besichtigen) Warum ______________ ihr nicht mal Schloss Sanssouci?
6. (kennen) Wir ______________ das Schloss schon so gut.
7. (holen) Was ______________ du denn im Supermarkt?
8. (brauchen) Ich ______________ Fleisch zum Grillen.
9. (haben) Warum ______________ du keinen Hunger?
10. (sein) Wann ______________ du heute zu Hause?

D. Fill in each blank with the correct form of the verb in parentheses. Note that all of these verbs have irregular forms.

1. (geben) Was **gibt** Marga ihrer Mutter zum Muttertag?
2. (geben) Sie ______________ ihr eine Schachtel Pralinen.
3. (wissen) Ich ______________ nicht, was ich Mutti schenken soll.
4. (wissen) Muttertag ist morgen! Und du ______________ das nicht?
5. (laufen) Wann ______________ du wieder einmal Skateboard?
6. (laufen) Mein Bruder ______________ Skateboard, ich nicht.
7. (fahren) Wann ______________ du denn nach Florida?
8. (fahren) Meine Kusine ________ im Mai; ich ______________ nicht.
9. (haben) Wo ________ ihr denn das Brot gekauft?

E. Write the following sentences in German.

1. What are you doing? **Was machst du?**
2. I'm playing cards. ______________
3. Does Mike play cards? ______________
4. No, but he does play chess. ______________
5. What are you reading? ______________
6. I'm reading a book. ______________
7. Are you writing an e-mail? ______________
8. Yes, I'm writing Mom an e-mail. ______________
9. You do write a lot! ______________

KAPITEL 2 (WIEDERHOLUNG)

MODAL VERBS (REVIEW)

Pupil's Edition, p. 37

Compare Both English and German have a set of **helping verbs**, often referred to as **modal verbs** (or modal auxiliaries), that are used with other verbs **to express mood** or possibility. The modal verbs are conjugated for person and number, and they can be used with an infinitive (unconjugated verb). Here are the German modal verbs that you should know:

Modals		Examples	
können	*can*	Ich kann gehen.	*I can go.*
dürfen	*may*	Du darfst gehen.	*You may go.*
müssen	*must*	Er muss gehen.	*He must go.*
sollen	*should*	Sie soll gehen.	*She should go.*
wollen	*want to*	Wir wollen gehen.	*We want to go.*
möchte-forms	*would like to*	Sie möchten gehen.	*They would like to go.*

The German modals have these forms in the present tense, using **können** as an example:

	Singular			Plural	
Ich	kann	nichts essen.	Wir	könn**en**	nichts essen.
Du	kann**st**	nichts essen.	Ihr	könn**t**	nichts essen.
Er, sie, es	kann	nichts essen.	Sie	könn**en**	nichts essen.

What do you notice about the different verb forms?

A. Fill in each blank with the correct form of the modal verb given in parentheses.

1. (müssen) Wann **musst** du zu Hause helfen?
2. (dürfen) Wir ______________ heute nicht ins Kino gehen.
3. (können) Warum ______________ ihr eure Hausaufgaben nicht machen?
4. (wollen) Ich ______________ heute zuerst meine Oma anrufen.
5. (sollen) Warum ______________ wir schon wieder Tennis spielen?
6. (möchte-form) Was ______________ du denn zum Geburtstag haben?
7. (wollen) Ich glaube, du ______________ jetzt etwas essen.
8. (müssen) Wer von euch ______________ zu Hause bleiben?
9. (können) Ich ______________ heute nicht einkaufen gehen.

B. Write sentences using a modal verb, an infinitive, and all the other information given.

1. die Kinder / dürfen / essen / kein Eis **Die Kinder dürfen kein Eis essen.**
2. ich / wollen / anziehen / die Jeans ____________________
3. du / können / anrufen / mich / später ____________________
4. John / müssen / mähen / den Rasen ____________________
5. ihr / möchte-form / gehen / ins Kino ____________________
6. Jennie / sollen / kaufen / den Kuchen ____________________
7. du / müssen / essen / viel Obst ____________________
8. möchte-form / du / trinken / Saft / ? ____________________

C. Write these sentences in German.

1. We must go home now. **Wir müssen jetzt nach Hause gehen.**
2. I would like to eat at 2 o'clock. ____________________
3. The children may drink juice. ____________________
4. Jenna wants to buy shoes. ____________________
5. He should go home. ____________________
6. I must read the book. ____________________
7. Can you believe that? ____________________
8. She would like to play tennis now. ____________________

MEANINGS OF MODAL VERBS (REVIEW) *Pupil's Edition, p. 37*

Compare When talking about **mood** we refer to verbs, such as the **modals**, that express functions such as *ability, desire, possibility,* and so on.

dürfen, *may, to be allowed to,* expresses the function of asking for or granting permission
Darf ich heute ins Kino gehen?

können, *can, to be able to,* expresses the function of being able to do something, or knowing a skill
Kannst du bitte für mich die Fenster putzen? Kannst du Deutsch?

wollen, *to want to,* expresses the function of wish, desire, or intention
Was wollt ihr heute machen? Wir wollen Fußball spielen.

sollen, *should, to be supposed to,* expresses the function of obligation
Wo sollen wir das Brot kaufen? Sollen wir das Obst beim Gemüsehändler kaufen?

müssen, *must, to have to,* expresses the function of necessity or compulsion
Ich muss heute meine Hausaufgaben machen.

möchte-forms, *would like (to),* express the function of wish or desire
Möchtest du mit mir in eine Disko gehen?

A. Write sentences using what you know about the various meanings of the modals.

(den Opa anrufen)
1. We can call grandpa. **Wir können den Opa anrufen.**
2. We want to call grandpa. ______
3. We're supposed to call grandpa. ______
4. We would like to call grandpa. ______
5. We must call grandpa. ______
6. We are allowed to call grandpa. ______

B. Write sentences using what you know about the various meaning of the modals.

(nach Hause gehen)
1. I don't want to go home. **Ich will nicht nach Hause gehen.**
2. I would not like to go home. ______
3. I must not go home. ______
4. I'm not supposed to go home. ______
5. I cannot go home. ______
6. We are not allowed to go home. ______

C. Write sentences using what you know about the various meanings of the modals.

(heute Tennis spielen)

1. He wants to play tennis today. **Er will heute Tennis spielen.**
2. He would like to play tennis today. ____________
3. He must play tennis today. ____________
4. He can play tennis today. ____________
5. He is supposed to play tennis today. ____________
6. We may play tennis today. ____________

D. Write these English sentences in German.

1. I would like to go to the movies. **Ich möchte ins Kino gehen.**
2. I want to see *Gladiator.* ____________
3. I can go at 5 o'clock. ____________
4. I must do my homework. ____________
5. Do you know German? ____________
6. I know German and English. ____________
7. Can you play chess? ____________
8. Why do you have to stay at home? ____________

SUBJECTS, DIRECT AND INDIRECT OBJECTS (REVIEW)

Pupil's Edition, pp. 41, 50

In English The **subject** of a sentence is the thing or the person that performs the action; the **direct object** is the recipient of the action, and the **indirect object** tells *to whom* or *to what,* or *for whom* or *for what,* the action of the verb is done. Subjects, direct objects, and indirect objects can be single nouns, noun phrases, or pronouns.

SUBJECT		INDIRECT OBJECT	DIRECT OBJECT
The rich daughter	bought	her mother	a beautiful present.
She	gave	her	an expensive watch.
SUBJECT		**INIRECT OBJECT**	**DIRECT OBJECT**
My grandfather	bought	my little brother	a surprise.
He	gave	him	a bicycle.

A. Underline the subject, direct object, and indirect object, then label each one S (subject), DO (direct object), or IO (indirect object).

1. My girlfriend (S) bought her cousin (IO) a magazine subscription (DO).
2. My cousin gave her sister a beautiful bracelet.
3. Michael lent his classmate ten euros.
4. Andrea wrote her grandparents a long letter.
5. My sister and I sent our cousins an e-mail.
6. Julia and Mark sent their math teacher a fax.

KAPITEL 2

In German As in English, the **subject** of a sentence is the thing or the person that performs the action; the **direct object** is the recipient of the action, and the **indirect object** tells *to whom* or *to what,* or *for whom* or *for what,* the action of the verb is done. Subjects, direct objects, and indirect objects can be single nouns, noun phrases, or pronouns. In German, subjects, direct objects, and indirect objects all have particular case forms.

1. Subjects are always in the **nominative case**:

Der Opa / mein Vater / er war im Dezember in Spanien.
Meine Mutter / die Oma / sie hört gern Musik.

2. Direct objects are in the **accusative case**:

Ich habe meinen Opa / den Vati / ihn in Spanien besucht.
Wir besuchen unsere Oma / die Tante Erna / sie morgen Abend.

3. Indirect objects are in the **dative case**:

Wir schenken unserem Opa / dem Vati / ihm eine Uhr zum Vatertag.
Ich kaufe der Mutti / unserer Oma / ihr Pralinen zum Geburtstag.

Since case is clearly marked, German sentences can start with a direct or an indirect object.

Den Kuchen hat meine Mutter dem Opa gekauft.	(direct object)
Dem Opa hat meine Mutter einen Kuchen gekauft.	(indirect object)

B. Underline the subject, direct object, and indirect object, then label each one S (subject), DO (direct object), or IO (indirect object).

1. Die Eltern (S) haben meiner Schwester (IO) ein tolles Buch (DO) geschenkt.
2. Ein neues Auto hat der Vati gestern meiner Mutti gekauft.
3. Meinem Bruder hat die Mutti heute eine CD gegeben.
4. Eine E-Mail schicken die Kinder ihren Eltern heute.
5. Den Großeltern schicken die Eltern einen Blumenstrauß.
6. Was schenken denn deine Geschwister deinen Eltern zum Hochzeitstag?
7. Dem neuen Deutschlehrer schenken die Schüler einen Kalender.
8. Und ein Buch über Bach schenken die Musikschüler ihrem Musiklehrer.
9. Unserer Biolehrerin geben viele Schüler ein Buch über Tiere.

C. Fill in the first blank with the correct form of the definite article, and the second blank with the correct form of the indefinite article.

1. Wir kaufen __dem__ Vati __einen__ Kalender zum Geburtstag.
2. Ich schenke ________ Mutti ________ Pulli zum Geburtstag.
3. Du gibst doch ________ Onkel Paul ________ Kuchen zum Namenstag.
4. Schenkst du ________ Großvater ________ CD zu Weihnachten?
5. Gibst du ________ Großmutter ________ Buch zum Geburtstag?
6. Kaufst du ________ Tante Holly ________ T-Shirt?
7. Mark schenkt ________ Ellen ________ Handy zum Geburtstag.
8. Und ich kaufe ________ Mark ________ Armbanduhr.

KAPITEL 2

D. Fill in each blank with the correct personal pronoun.

1. Wann besuchst du deinen Opa? Ich besuche __ihn__ morgen.
2. Was schenkst du deinem Opa? Ich schenke ________ ein Buch.
3. Hast du die Biolehrerin gern? Ich habe ________ sehr gern.
4. Was kaufst du der Lehrerin? Ich kaufe ________ eine CD.
5. Isst du den Spinat gern? Ich esse ________ sehr gern.
6. Isst du den Kuchen nicht? Ich esse ________ heute Abend.
7. Was schenkst du denn deiner Kusine? Ich schenke ________ einen Tennisschläger.
8. Und was kaufst du deinem Cousin? Ich kaufe ________ einen Gürtel.

KAPITEL 3

■ PAST TENSE

Pupil's Edition, p. 66

Compare In English and in German, several different verb constructions are used to indicate that an action took place in the **past**. Study them closely. You will notice that German does not have some of the forms that English has.

TENSE	ENGLISH	GERMAN
simple past	we play**ed**	wir spielten
past progressive	we **were** play**ing**	—
past emphatic	we **did** play	—
present perfect	we **have** play**ed**	wir **haben ge**spiel**t**
past perfect	we **had** play**ed**	wir **hatten ge**spiel**t**
future perfect	we **will have** play**ed**	wir **werden ge**spiel**t haben**

The simple past is called "simple" because it consists of only one word. The "perfect" tenses shown here all include a form of **have** or **haben** plus a verb form called the *past participle* that expresses the action. In this chapter, only the simple past and the present perfect will be discussed.

A. Read these sentences and determine whether the simple past or the present perfect tense is used. Check the appropriate column.

	SIMPLE PAST	PRESENT PERFECT
1. I visited my grandparents in Florida.	✓	____
2. I never saw this movie.	____	____
3. When have you heard him sing?	____	____
4. Margit has returned to school.	____	____
5. Where has she spent her vacation?	____	____
6. She went to Europe with her parents.	____	____
7. They stayed at a youth hostel.	____	____
8. Have you ever stayed at a youth hostel?	____	____

B. Read these German sentences and determine the tense used to express past time. Check the appropriate column. Remember: the simple past uses one verb, the present perfect tense uses two.

	SIMPLE PAST	PRESENT PERFECT
1. Wir haben den ganzen Tag gearbeitet.	______	✓
2. Hans spielte am Sonntag Fußball.	______	______
3. Was hast du deiner Mutter geschenkt?	______	______
4. Wir haben in einer Pension gewohnt.	______	______
5. Was habt ihr den ganzen Tag gemacht?	______	______
6. Wir haben gefaulenzt.	______	______
7. Wir wohnten in einer Jugendherberge.	______	______

C. Which past participle logically completes each sentence? Choose a past participle from the list below.

besucht	fotografiert	gefahren	gegangen	gegessen
gelesen	gemacht	gesehen	gespielt	gewohnt

1. Ich habe meine Tante in Frankfurt ______ **besucht** ______ .
2. Wir haben in einer Pension in Tirol ______________________ .
3. Wir haben in einem Gasthaus ______________________ .
4. Ich habe mit meiner Kamera viel ______________________ .
5. Ich habe mit meinem Freund Tennis ______________________ .
6. Was hast du denn in den Ferien ______________________ ?
7. Ich bin mit meinen Eltern an den Bodensee ______________________ .
8. Das Wetter war schlecht, und ich habe viele Bücher ______________________ .
9. Wir sind auch oft ins Kino ______________________ .
10. Wir haben ganz tolle Filme ______________________ .

D. How would you summarize what you have learned about the past tense?

____

____

PAST PARTICIPLES

In English A **past participle** is a verb form that expresses the action in perfect tenses. Every verb has its own past participle form. The past participle is always used with a conjugated form of **have** (the past participle form itself cannot be conjugated).

PRESENT PERFECT

We **have worked** in the garden. (past participle: **worked**)
Basti **has gone** to his grandparents' house. (past participle: **gone**)

Past participles can be **regular** or **irregular**. A regular past participle is formed using a predictable pattern: you always add **-ed** or **-d** to the plain verb.

(walk) I have walk**ed**
(visit) I have visit**ed**
(hike) I have hike**d**
(live) I have live**d**
(help) I have help**ed**
(learn) I have learn**ed**

An irregular past participle does not follow the pattern. The most common way to form irregular past participles is with a vowel change. Some past participles look just like the infinitive. When non-English-speakers study English, they must memorize the irregular past participle forms.

(bring) I have brought
(speak) I have spoken
(sing) I have sung
(found) I have found
(eat) I have eaten
(stand) I have stood

A. Underline the regular past participles. Circle the irregular past participles.

1. We have hiked all over the Alps and have seen many interesting sights.
2. I have reminded you so often, and yet you still have not written that letter.
3. Have you hidden the presents you bought yesterday?
4. Daniel and Laura have already been to Munich, but they haven't visited Hamburg.
5. Pauline has acted as if my feelings don't matter.
6. I have worn that coat for so many years that I have become tired of it.
7. Have you received the package, or have you called about it?
8. I have cut the cake, but I haven't got enough forks.
9. I've already washed those pants, and they haven't shrunk.
10. Erika has given her allowance to charity instead of buying the toy she wanted.

In German As in English, German verbs are classified as regular or irregular. Verbs that have a regular past participle are referred to as "weak verbs." The **past participles of weak verbs** always end in **-t**. They also have the prefix **ge-**.

INFINITIVE	VERB STEM	PAST PARTICIPLE
spielen	spiel-	**ge**spiel**t**
machen	mach-	**ge**mach**t**

Verbs that have irregular past participle forms are called "strong verbs." As with English irregular verbs, they often have a vowel change or other spelling change. The **past participles of strong verbs** begin with **ge-** and always end in **-en** or **-n**.

INFINITIVE	VERB STEM	PAST PARTICIPLE
laufen	lauf-	**ge**lauf**en**
finden	find-	**ge**f**u**nd**en**
gehen	geh-	**gegangen**

Note the following:

a. Verbs that already have an inseparable prefix do NOT add the prefix **ge-**.

besuchen	besuch**t**
gefallen	gefallen

b. Verbs whose infinitive ends in **-ieren** also do not add the prefix **ge-**.

fotografieren	fotografiert

c. Verbs with separable prefixes have the prefix **ge-** between the separable prefix and the verb.

aussehen	aus**ge**sehen
mitkommen	mit**ge**kommen

Note: There is no way of predicting the form of the past participle of a strong verb in German. You simply must memorize the form of the past participle.

B. Underline all past participles of weak verbs and circle all past participles of strong verbs.

1. Am Nachmittag sind wir in die Stadt (gegangen) und haben Klamotten gekauft.
2. In den Ferien habe ich viel gegessen und gelesen.
3. Ich habe gehört, du hast deinem Freund Pralinen geschenkt.
4. Wir sind den ganzen Tag gelaufen und haben danach noch Tennis gespielt.
5. Ich habe ein Museum besichtigt und bin danach mit Mutti ins Kino gegangen.
6. Hast du ein gutes Buch gelesen, oder hast du nur gefaulenzt?

C. Underline the conjugated verbs and circle the past participles.

1. Wir sind nach Bayern (gefahren,) und wir haben dort meine Großeltern (besucht.)
2. Ich habe viel gefilmt, und wir haben sehr viel gesehen.
3. Wir sind nach Garmisch gefahren und sind dort zwei Wochen geblieben.
4. Wir haben in einer Pension gewohnt und haben in tollen Lokalen gegessen.
5. Wir sind oft in den Bergen gewandert, und ich habe auch viel geschwommen.
6. Ich habe in den Bergen viel fotografiert, und ich habe tolle Dias gemacht.
7. Ich habe mir auch ein prima Buch gekauft und habe viel gelesen.

D. How would you summarize what you have learned about German past participles?

____

PRESENT PERFECT

In English The **present perfect** is a tense that refers to **past time**. It is made up of two verb forms: a conjugated form of **to have**, and a **past participle**.

I **have walked** to school every day this week.
It **has** not **rained** in weeks.
We **have** not **taken** the bus to school this semester.

A. Underline the helping verb and circle the past participle.

1. Have you seen the Schmidt's new car?
2. She has not yet heard if she won.
3. They have eaten the pizza, but they haven't drunk all the soda.
4. Whoever has left gum on the counter must clean it up.
5. I have read her other books, but I haven't heard about the latest one.
6. I found your letter, but I have not read it yet.
7. The Müllers have gone on vacation; they have flown to the coast of Spain.

In German As in English, the **present perfect tense** consists of a **helping verb** and the **past participle**. Most of the time the helping verb is a conjugated form of **haben**. However, some past participles use a conjugated form of **sein** as the helping verb.

Was **habt** ihr gestern **gemacht**?
Wir **haben** am Abend Tennis **gespielt**.
Ich **bin** gestern Abend ins Kino **gegangen**.

Notice that the past participle is placed at the end of each sentence, while the helping verb is in the normal verb position. (Can you think of another construction that uses two verbs, with one of them at the end of the sentence?)

The helping verb **haben** is used with all transitive verbs (verbs that can have a direct object), and intransitive verbs (verbs that don't take a direct object) that express a condition or an event in its duration.

Ich **habe** die Berge fotografiert.	(die Berge: direct object)
Wir **haben** einmal in Berlin gewohnt.	(an event that lasted awhile)

The helping verb **sein** is used with verbs that indicate a change of place or condition.

Wir **sind** in die Stadt gefahren.	(We went from one place to another.)
Ich **bin** um 11 Uhr eingeschlafen.	(You were awake and then went to sleep.)

B. Underline the helping verb and circle the past participle.

1. Wir sind nach Mittenwald gefahren und haben dort in einer Pension gewohnt.
2. Wo bist du in den Ferien gewesen und was hast du alles gemacht?
3. Ich bin zu Hause geblieben und habe gefaulenzt.
4. Hast du gehört, wer gekommen ist?
5. Wir haben Musik gespielt, und es ist sehr laut gewesen.
6. Wer hat denn gesehen, wann du einmal gearbeitet hast?

C. In each of the following sentences, determine if the past participle indicates a change of place or condition, or if the verb is transitive and has a direct object.

	Change of Place	Direct Object
1. Ich habe eine Pizza gegessen.	_____	✓
2. Wir sind sehr viel gewandert.	_____	_____
3. Mein Vater hat die Berge gefilmt.	_____	_____
4. Er ist mit dem Auto nach Erfurt gefahren.	_____	_____
5. Sie hat das Auto in die Garage gefahren.	_____	_____
6. Wir sind um den See spaziert.	_____	_____

D. Fill in the blanks with the correct form of **haben** or **sein** and the past participle of the verb in parentheses.

1. (lesen) Ich ___**habe**___ ein interessantes Buch ___**gelesen**___ .
2. (laufen) Warum ____________ ihr nicht um den See ________________ ?
3. (machen) Meine Freundin ____________ am Wochenende nichts ________________ .
4. (fahren) Ich ____________ mit meinen Eltern nach Berlin ________________ .
5. (fahren) Ich habe den Führerschein und ____________ Vatis Auto ________________ .
6. (sein) Ich ____________ eine Woche in Berlin ________________ .
7. (gehen) Wir ____________ in den Zoo ________________ .
8. (sehen) Und wir ____________ den neuen Reichstag ________________ .
9. (besuchen) Sag, ____________ du auch das Pergamonmuseum ________________ ?

E. Summarize what you have learned about the use of **haben** or **sein** as a helping verb in sentences with the present perfect.

____

____

USE OF THE PRESENT PERFECT TENSE

Compare In both English and German, the **past tense** is structurally similar; however, the usage of the various past-tense forms differs between the languages. Look at these sentences and notice the different ways the past is expressed:

Wir sind ins Kino gegangen.	We went to the movies.
Was habt ihr gesehen?	What did you see?
Wir haben „Gladiator" gesehen.	We saw *Gladiator.*
Wie hat dir der Film gefallen?	How did you like the movie?
Der Film hat mir sehr gut gefallen.	I liked the movie very much.

In German To express past time, you can always use the **present perfect tense**. The present perfect tense is used to refer to past time, especially in conversation, and is virtually the only tense used to express past time in Austria, Switzerland, and the southern parts of Germany.

Note: There is a *simple past* in German, like *did, saw, went.* This simple past is used more in narration.

A. In the following dialogs, fill in the blanks with the correct forms of the helping verb and an appropriate past participle.

Mark und Sara

1. Mark: Ich **bin** in den Ferien mit meiner GAPP-Klasse in Sachsen **gewesen**.
2. Sara: Wie lange ________ ihr dort ________________?
3. Und wo ________ ihr ________________?
4. Mark: Wir ________ eine Woche in Dresden ________________.
5. Sara: Was ________ du die ganze Zeit ________________?
6. Mark: Ich ________ mit den deutschen Schülern Fussball ________________.
7. Sara: Du ________ in Dresden bestimmt viel ________________.
8. Mark: Wir ________ viele Museen ________________.
9. Sara: Du ________ sicher auch im Zwinger ________________, ja?
10. Mark: Natürlich! Und wir ________ sogar einmal in die Oper ________________.

Uhma und Clark

11. Uhma: Wo **hast** du denn heute zu Mittag **gegessen**?
12. Clark: Wir ________ in ein prima Restaurant ________________.
13. Uhma: Was ________ ihr am Nachmittag ________________?
14. Clark: Ich ________ im Garten ________________, und mein Freund,
15. der Robert, ________ für mich den Müll ________________.

16. Uhma: Ich __________ meiner Mutter in der Küche __________________ ;

17. ich __________ das Geschirr __________________ , die Fenster

18. ____________ , und ich __________ einkaufen __________________ .

19. Clark: Da __________ du aber sehr fleißig __________________ .

B. How would you express the English sentences in German?

1. I played Tennis. **Ich habe Tennis gespielt.**
2. We went to the city. ______________________________
3. We saw a movie. ______________________________
4. Then I visited friends. ______________________________
5. We played cards. ______________________________
6. And we ate a pizza. ______________________________
7. What did you do? ______________________________
8. I read a book. ______________________________
9. I did not read the magazine. ______________________________
10. Did you read the book? ______________________________

C. Summarize what you know about the usage of the German present perfect.

____

____

____

KAPITEL 3

PREPOSITIONS: DIRECTION VS. LOCATION

In English A **preposition** is a word that shows the relationship of a noun or pronoun to the rest of the sentence. Some common prepositions are **by, with, on, through**. A **prepositional phrase** consists of the preposition, the object of the preposition, and any articles or modifiers. The object of a preposition is always a noun or a pronoun.

My parents went **to** the Baltic Sea.
I spent this afternoon **at** our beautiful beach.

A. Circle the preposition(s) and underline the prepositional phrase(s) in each of the following sentences.

1. The squirrel ran up the tree and leapt onto the roof.
2. I'm going to the store – is there anything else I should write on the shopping list?
3. You'll have to see the pictures of our vacation to California.
4. Our house is past the park, near the big church.
5. I was at the movies with my friends.
6. Going through that experience was a turning point in my life.
7. If the cat isn't underneath the bed, try looking above the dryer.
8. Are we to make our beds before breakfast, or can we do without it this time?

In German **Prepositions** require the object of the preposition and its modifiers to be in a certain case.

Ich komme **mit** **dem Rad** zur Schule. (**mit**: dative case)
Wartest du **auf** **mich**? (**auf**: accusative case)

The following prepositions, **an, auf, in, über, unter, hinter, neben, vor, zwischen,** are followed by either dative or accusative case forms, depending on the situation.

a. When these prepositions indicate **location** (in answer to a question beginning with **wo?**), **dative case** forms must be used.

Wo warst du? Ich war **in der Stadt**.
Wo sitzt ihr? Wir sitzen **hinter dir**.

b. When these prepositions indicate **direction** (in answer to a question beginning with **wohin?**), **accusative case** forms must be used.

Wohin fahrt ihr? Wir fahren **in die Stadt**.
Wohin setzt ihr euch? Wir setzen uns **hinter dich**.

It is important to get a feeling for what is location and what is direction.

B. Circle the prepositions and underline the prepositional phrases in the following sentences.

1. Wir waren schon im Gebirge, und jetzt fahren wir an die Nordsee.
2. Heute gehen wir ins Kino, denn gestern waren wir in der Oper.
3. Meine Mutter war eben im Garten. Ich glaube, sie ist in die Küche gegangen.
4. Warst du schon im Museum, oder gehst du jetzt erst ins Museum?
5. Ich war in der Türkei und fahre jetzt in die Schweiz.
6. Wann fährst du an die Nordsee? Ich war einmal an der Ostsee. Einfach toll!

C. Do the following expressions indicate location or direction? Check the appropriate column.

	LOCATION	DIRECTION
1. Auf ins Gebirge!	_____	✓
2. Schwimm in der Nordsee!	_____	_____
3. Warum ist es am Rhein so schön!	_____	_____
4. Rein ins Wasser!	_____	_____
5. Am Pillersee waren wir.	_____	_____
6. Bergsteigen in den Alpen	_____	_____
7. Unsere Reise an den Bodensee	_____	_____
8. Gehen wir ins Café Mozart!	_____	_____

D. Which interrogative would you use to answer these statements? Fill in each blank with **Wo** or **Wohin**.

1. Wir fahren ins Gebirge. **Wohin** fahrt ihr?
2. Ich war an der Nordsee. ________________ warst du?
3. Frank fährt nach Dresden. ________________ fährt Frank?
4. Elke war im Gebirge. ________________ war Elke?
5. Wir waren am Bodensee. ________________ wart ihr?
6. Ich gehe in die Oper. ________________ gehst du?
7. Ich fahre in die Stadt. ________________ fährst du?
8. Ich war schon in der Stadt. ________________ warst du schon?

E. Summarize what you have learned about German prepositions that can indicate either direction or location.

____

____

KAPITEL 3

■ INDIRECT OBJECT PRONOUNS

Pupil's Edition, p. 77

In English Pronouns can be used as subjects or as objects. The object pronouns are different from the subject pronouns. Compare these forms:

Singular		Plural	
Subject Pronouns	Object Pronouns	Subject Pronouns	Object Pronouns
I	me	we	us
you	you	you	you
he	him		
she	her	they	them
it	it		

A. In the following sentences, underline the subject pronouns and circle the object pronouns.

1. We saw her in Frankfurt.
2. She invited us to go to a concert.
3. They bought me a very expensive ticket.
4. I gave them 5 euros.
5. How many times did they call you?
6. They called me five times.
7. When did you invite them for lunch?

In German German also has subject and object pronouns. However, the object pronouns have different forms when they are **direct objects** or **indirect objects**. Direct object pronouns are in the accusative case, indirect object pronouns are in the dative case.

Wir haben Ferien gemacht.	(wir—subject pronoun, nominative case)
Hast du **uns** angerufen?	(uns—direct object pronoun, accusative case)
Ich habe **ihr** eine Kinokarte gekauft.	(ihr—indirect object, dative case)
Und eine Karte war für **mich**.	(mich—object of the preposition **für**, accusative case)

There are some special verbs in German that require the **direct object** to be in the **dative case**. Some of these verbs are: **antworten**, **danken**, **gefallen**, **helfen**.

Warum antwortest du **mir** nicht?
Ich danke **dir** für das Geschenk.
Deutschland hat **ihnen** sehr gut gefallen.

Here is a list of the German subject pronouns, direct object pronouns, and indirect object pronouns.

SUBJECT PRONOUNS NOMINATIVE	DIRECT OBJECT PRONOUNS ACCUSATIVE	INDIRECT OBJECT PRONOUNS DATIVE
ich	mich	mir
du	dich	dir
er	ihn	ihm
sie	sie	ihr
es	es	ihm
wir	uns	uns
ihr	euch	euch
sie *(they)*	sie	ihnen
Sie *(you)*	Sie	Ihnen

B. In the following sentences, underline all accusative-case direct object pronouns, and circle all indirect object pronouns or direct object pronouns that are in the dative case.

1. Wir haben sie angerufen, aber wir haben ihnen nicht im Garten geholfen.
2. Ich gebe euch gern das Buch, aber ich habe euch nicht gesehen.
3. Der Pulli hat ihr nicht gefallen, und sie hat ihn nicht gekauft.
4. Hast du ihr ein Geschenk gekauft, und hat sie dich nicht angerufen?
5. Ich habe ihm geschrieben, aber er hat mir nicht geantwortet.
6. Hast du sie gestern besucht, und hast du ihnen das Buch gegeben?
7. Kann ich Ihnen eine Zeitung geben, oder kann ich Sie sofort zum Chef bringen?
8. Warum hast du ihnen nicht geantwortet, als sie dich gerufen haben?
9. Ich habe dir das Buch geschenkt, weil es dir so gut gefallen hat.

C. Fill in each blank with an appropriate pronoun.

1. Kennst du meinen Opa? Du kannst **ihm** mal eine Karte schreiben, und er ruft **dich** bestimmt danach an.
2. Herr Müller, wie hat _______ Bayern gefallen? Ich habe _______ lange nicht gesehen.
3. Wo ist die Renate? Ich will _______ das Buch geben, aber ich kann _______ nicht finden.
4. Wo seid ihr beiden? Ich suche _______ , und ich hab _______ schon einmal angerufen.
5. Du, Sara, ich hab _______ im Kino gesehen. Wie hat _______ der Film gefallen?
6. Hallo, Marco! Wann gibst du _______ das Buch zurück? Gefällt es _______ nicht?
7. Wo der Boris ist? Ich habe _______ in einer Imbissstube gesehen. Ich glaube, die Würstchen haben _______ dort gut geschmeckt.

D. Summarize what you have learned about indirect object pronouns.

____

KAPITEL 4

REFLEXIVE PRONOUNS

Pupil's Edition, p. 102

KAPITEL 4

In English A **reflexive pronoun** refers to the subject and is necessary to the meaning of the sentence. In English, the reflexive pronouns end in **-self** in the singular and in **-selves** in the plural.

I wash **myself** three times a day.
We hurt **ourselves** playing soccer.

A. Underline the reflexive pronouns in these sentences.

1. Don't blame yourself for losing the game.
2. He is congratulating himself for his three goals.
3. We pride ourselves in our success.
4. Did you cut yourself on the rock?
5. Martin forced himself to stay awake and finish his term paper.
6. Give yourselves a pat on the back!
7. The managers awarded themselves bonuses, even as the company went bankrupt.
8. Erika told herself that the party didn't matter anyway.
9. Hi, Max, help yourself to a soda!
10. The dog did itself a favor by leaving that snake alone.

Compare German also has **reflexive pronouns** for each of the different personal pronouns. However, German uses the direct object pronouns for the first and second persons and has a special reflexive form for the third person pronouns and the formal address.

	English			German	
PRONOUN	VERB	REFLEX. PRONOUN	PRONOUN	VERB	REFLEX. PRONOUN
I	wash	myself.	Ich	wasche	mich.
You	wash	yourself.	Du	wäschst	dich.
He	washes	himself.	Er	wäscht	**sich**.
She	washes	herself.	Sie	wäscht	**sich**.
It	washes	itself.	Es	wäscht	**sich**.
We	wash	ourselves.	Wir	waschen	uns.
You	wash	yourselves.	Ihr	wascht	euch.
They	wash	themselves.	Sie	waschen	**sich**.

KAPITEL 4

B. Underline the personal pronouns and circle the reflexive pronouns in these German sentences.

1. Wir waschen uns dreimal am Tag.
2. Ich schneide mich ab und zu in den Finger.
3. Und die Anja, sie schneidet sich nie.
4. Warum wäschst du dich nicht?
5. Wascht ihr euch nach dem Fußballspiel?
6. Der Max? Er wäscht sich immer nach dem Spiel.
7. Sag mal, wie hältst du dich fit?
8. Ich jogge und schwimme. So halte ich mich fit.

C. Fill in each blank with the correct reflexive pronoun.

1. Wann wäschst du ____dich____ ?
2. Ich wasche ________________ am Abend nach dem Tennisspiel.
3. Weißt du, wann ________________ der Oskar wäscht?
4. Ich weiß das nicht, aber wir waschen ________________ oft.
5. Wann wascht ihr ________________ denn?
6. Die Kinder waschen ________________ nach dem Spielen.
7. Herr Becker, waschen Sie ________________ nach dem Fußballspiel?

D. How would you summarize what you have learned about reflexive pronouns?

____

____

____

REFLEXIVE VERBS

Pupil's Edition, p. 102

In English Verbs that can have a reflexive pronoun as their object can also have non-reflexive nouns or pronouns as their objects.

I see **myself** in the mirror.	reflexive
I see **you** in the mirror.	not reflexive (personal pronoun)

A. Read the following sentences and determine whether the pronoun used is a personal pronoun or a reflexive pronoun. Check the appropriate column.

	Personal Pronoun	Reflexive Pronoun
1. Mary smiled at him.	✓	_____
2. Mary smiled at herself in the mirror.	_____	_____
3. The firefighter pulled him out of the river.	_____	_____
4. The firefighter pulled himself out of the river.	_____	_____
5. I'll buy a loaf of bread for myself.	_____	_____
6. I'll buy a loaf of bread for him.	_____	_____

Compare There are some verbs in German that can be used reflexively or not, as in English.

Ich sehe **mich** im Spiegel.	reflexive
Ich sehe **dich** im Spiegel.	not reflexive

However, there are many verbs in German that are used with reflexive pronouns. Such verbs are called **reflexive verbs**. The English equivalents of these verbs are not used with reflexive pronouns.

Ich **fühle mich** wohl.	I feel well.
Wie **hältst** du **dich** fit?	How do you keep fit?
Wir **freuen uns**, dass . . .	We are happy that . . .
Wiebke **ernährt sich** richtig.	Wiebke eats and drinks healthfully.

The infinitive form of reflexive verbs are always listed with the reflexive pronoun **sich**, or with its abbreviation, **s**.

Here is a list of the personal pronouns and the reflexive pronouns:

Subject Pronoun	Reflexive Pronoun (Accusative)	English
ich	mich	myself
du	dich	yourself
er/ sie/ es	sich	himself herself itself
wir	uns	ourselves
ihr	euch	yourselves
sie	sich	themselves
Sie (formal)	sich	yourself

KAPITEL 4

B. Underline the personal pronouns and circle the reflexive pronouns in these German sentences.

1. Ich frage dich, wie du (dich) fit hältst.
2. Wir fragen euch, wie ihr euch ernährt.
3. Darf ich Sie fragen, Herr Meier, wie Sie sich fühlen?
4. Du möchtest mich wohl fragen, wie ich mich ernähre.
5. Freut ihr euch nicht, dass ihr euch so wohl fühlt?
6. Ich freue mich, dass ihr euch so fit haltet.

C. Read the sentences above again and write the reflexive verbs as you find them listed in the vocabulary or in a dictionary.

sich fit halten ______________________________

____

D. Read the following sentences and write the appropriate reflexive pronoun in the space provided.

1. Wir freuen **uns**, dass ihr **euch** hier so wohl fühlt.
2. Unser Lehrer freut ____________, dass wir ____________ fit halten.
3. Ich freue ____________, dass du ____________ jetzt richtig ernährst.
4. Freust du ____________ nicht, dass du ____________ jetzt so wohl fühlst?
5. Ihr freut ____________ doch, dass ihr ____________ so gut fit haltet.
6. Die Kinder freuen ____________, dass sie ____________ richtig ernähren.

E. Write the following sentences in German. All sentences must be used with a reflexive pronoun in German.

1. I keep fit. **Ich halte mich fit.**
2. How do you keep fit? ____________
3. We are not happy. ____________
4. I feel good. ____________
5. Do you feel good? ____________
6. He has a good diet. ____________
7. Do you eat and drink healthfully? ____________

F. Summarize what you have learned about reflexive verbs.

____

____

KAPITEL 5

POSSESSIVE ADJECTIVES

Pupil's Edition, p. 136

Definition: A **possessive adjective** (or a possessive for short) is a word that describes a noun by showing who or what possesses it.

> **I** am eating a sandwich. **My** sandwich is delicious.
> **We** have a new car. **Our** car sits in the garage.
> **The car's** color is blue. No, **its** color is black.

The English possessives are **my, your, his, her, its, our, your, their.**

A. Circle the possessive adjectives.

1. What do you have on (your) sandwich, John?
2. I have a piece of cheese on my sandwich.
3. Where did he buy his new car?
4. He bought his new car from a car dealer.
5. How did we get our car to run again?
6. They got their car to run again in no time.

Compare The German possessive adjectives also refer to the person or thing that possesses something or the quality it has. However, the ending of the possessive adjective must agree in gender, number, and case with the thing being possessed.

Ich esse ein Sandwich. **Mein** Sandwich ist lecker.	neuter/singular/nominative
Ich esse Joghurt. Möchtest du mein**en** Joghurt probieren?	masculine/singular/accusative
Ich esse Brot. Was hast du auf dein**em** Brot?	neuter/singular/dative after **auf**

Here is a comparison of the English possessive adjectives and their German equivalents.

my	**mein**
your (familiar, singular)	**dein**
his	**sein**
her	**ihr**
its	**sein**
our	**unser**
your (familiar, plural)	**euer**
their	**ihr**
your (formal, singular and plural)	**Ihr**

B. Read each sentence and circle the possessive adjective. Then identify the possessive adjective by gender, number, and case.

	Meaning	Gender	Case
1. Ich trinke (meinen) Kakao nicht.	my	masc.	acc.
2. Dein Pausenbrot sieht lecker aus.			
3. Ich gebe die Milch seinem Bruder.			
4. Sein Bruder trinkt Milch sehr gern.			
5. Wo hast du meine Schwester gesehen?			
6. Was hast du meiner Schwester gesagt?			
7. Hast du schon ihr Auto gesehen?			
8. Sein Rad war nicht sehr teuer.			
9. Wo ist denn nur unser Fußball?			

C. Fill in the correct form of the possessive adjective given in parentheses.

1. (my) Wer hat denn ___mein___ Pausenbrot gegessen?
2. (his) Ich habe ______________ Pausenbrot nicht gegessen.
3. (our) Wir haben ______________ Kakao nicht getrunken.
4. (her) Aber ich habe ______________ Kakao getrunken.
5. (her) Ich habe die Birnen ______________ Schwester gegeben.
6. (your) Hast du die Birnen ______________ Bruder gegeben?
7. (your) Warum haben Sie ______________ Joghurt nicht gegessen, Frau Sänger?
8. (their) Die Schüler haben ______________ Sandwiches nicht gegessen.
9. (our) Aber wer hat denn ______________ Obst gegessen?

D. Summarize what you have learned about German possessives.

____

____

____

INCLUSIVE COMMAND

Pupil's Edition, p. 159

In English The command form in English that includes the speaker is called the "let's command," or the **inclusive command**.

Let's go to the movies. Let's finish the game.

A. Are these regular commands or inclusive commands? Check the appropriate column.

	REGULAR	INCLUSIVE
1. Get the bread at the bakery.	✓	____
2. Let's buy the fruit at the supermarket.	____	____
3. Let's call our grandparents.	____	____
4. Go home immediately.	____	____
5. Let's go to concert tonight.	____	____
6. Buy all your groceries today.	____	____
7. Play this song again, please.	____	____
8. Let's not play it again.	____	____

In German The **inclusive command** uses the **wir**-form of the verb in the first position.

Gehen wir ins Kino! Let's go to the movies.
Bleiben wir zu Hause! Let's stay home.
Rufen wir die Maike an! Let's call Maike.

B. Are these sentences regular statements or inclusive commands? Check the appropriate column.

	STATEMENT	INCLUSIVE COMMAND
1. Um sieben Uhr gehen wir nach Hause.	✓	____
2. Gehen wir erst um fünf Uhr nach Hause.	____	____
3. Wir kaufen das Brot beim Bäcker.	____	____
4. Kaufen wir das Obst im Obstladen.	____	____
5. Besuchen wir doch mal deine Großeltern.	____	____
6. Morgen besuchen wir meine Oma.	____	____
7. Wir schreiben die Antwort an die Tafel.	____	____
8. Schreiben wir die Antwort lieber ins Heft.	____	____

C. Write an appropriate inclusive command in the space provided.

1. **Rufen wir** den Arzt an.
2. ______________ zum Arzt.
3. ______________ die Medizin in der Apotheke.
4. ______________ mal eine Pause!
5. ______________ die Sonnencreme mit dem Schutzfaktor 8.
6. ______________ heute nach der Schule Tennis.
7. ______________ mal den Max, ob er mitspielt.
8. ______________ jetzt ein Eis.

D. How would you express these commands in German?

1. Let's go to the supermarket. **Gehen wir zum Supermarkt.**
2. Let's call our grandma. ______________
3. Let's stay at home. ______________
4. Let's drink milk. ______________
5. Let's go along. ______________
6. Let's learn German. ______________
7. Let's eat now. ______________
8. Let's not say anything. ______________

E. Summarize what you have learned about the inclusive command.

____

____

____

KAPITEL 6

DIRECT OBJECTS IN THE DATIVE CASE

Pupil's Edition, p. 163

In English You have learned that transitive verbs take **direct objects**.

	Direct Objects	
The sneakers fit	the children	well.
We are helping	our grandparents	in the garden.

A. Circle the direct objects in these sentences.

1. Clayton, please answer (the question)
2. I'll thank you with dinner tomorrow night.
3. What ails the boy?
4. We can follow you to the theater.
5. These jeans don't fit me anymore.
6. The shoes are too small; they hurt my feet.

In German There are some German verbs that require a **direct object** to be in the **dative case**. Some of these verbs are:

antworten	*to answer*	**folgen**	*to follow*	**helfen**	*to help*
danken	*to thank*	**gehören**	*to belong (to)*	**passen**	*to fit*
fehlen	*to ail, be wrong*	**gefallen**	to like	**schmecken**	*to taste*
(gut) gehen	*to be well*			**wehtun**	*to hurt*

	Direct Object / Dative	
Die Turnschuhe passen	**den Kindern**	gut.
Wir helfen	**unseren Großeltern**	im Garten.
Die Stadt Dresden gefällt	**dem Frank / ihm**	sehr gut.

Verbs that can have a direct object in the dative case have to be memorized. An underlying explanation can be made as to why these verbs take the dative case.

antworten	to answer, to give an answer *to someone*	Er antwortet **den** Schüler**n**.
danken	to thank, to give thanks *to someone*	Ich danke **dir**.
helfen	to help, to give help *to someone*	Wir helfen **der** alt**en** Frau.

B. Read the following sentences and determine whether the verb is used with a direct object in the accusative case or a direct object in the dative case.

	Accusative	Dative
1. Wir haben unsere alte Oma sehr gern.	✓	_____
2. Wir helfen unserer alten Oma am Wochenende.	_____	_____
3. Warum fragst du deinen Deutschlehrer nicht?	_____	_____
4. Warum antwortest du deinem Deutschlehrer nicht?	_____	_____

	ACCUSATIVE	DATIVE
5. Das tolle Auto gehört meinem Freund Mark.	_____	_____
6. Das alte Auto braucht viel Benzin.	_____	_____
7. Die Pizza schmeckt mir sehr gut.	_____	_____
8. Die Pizza hat nur einen Fehler: sie ist zu klein!	_____	_____
9. Meine Schulter tut mir so weh.	_____	_____
10. Ich glaube, meine Schulter braucht eine Massage.	_____	_____

C. Fill in each blank with the correct form of the word or words given in parentheses.

1. (dein Opa) Warum hast du **deinem Opa** nicht geholfen?
2. (deine Oma) Hast du ____________________ schon geantwortet?
3. (du) Ich danke ____________________ für deine E-Mail.
4. (er) Weißt du, wie es ____________________ geht?
5. (die Renate) Ich glaube, ____________________ fehlt nichts.
6. (sie) Sie isst wieder. Das Essen schmeckt ____________________ gut.
7. (ihr) Max und Uli, warum tut ____________________ denn die Schulter weh?
8. (mein Bruder) Dieser Fußball gehört ____________________ .
9. (deine Mutter) Wie hat ____________________ das Spiel gefallen?
10. (das Auto) Wir sind ____________________ gefolgt.

D. Write these sentences in German.

1. Bobby, I'd like to help you. **Bobby, ich möchte dir helfen.**
2. This book belongs to me. ______________________________
3. Max, the sweater fits you well. ______________________________
4. I thank you, Augustin. ______________________________
5. Answer me, please! ______________________________
6. He likes the T-shirt. ______________________________
7. I like it, too. ______________________________
8. Who doesn't like the T-shirt? ______________________________
9. We don't like the T-shirt. ______________________________

E. Summarize the use of direct objects after certain verbs.

____

____

REFLEXIVE VERBS

In German There are many verbs in German that are used with reflexive pronouns. Such verbs are called **reflexive verbs**. The reflexive pronouns used in these sentences are in the **accusative case**. You have seen the following examples before.

Ich **fühle mich** wohl.	I feel well.
Wie **hältst** du **dich** fit?	How do you keep fit?
Wir **freuen uns**, dass . . .	We are happy that . . .
Wiebke **ernährt sich** richtig.	Wiebke eats and drinks healthfully.

When there is another object in the sentence, the reflexive pronoun must be in the **dative case**.

Ich verletze **mich** ab und zu.	accusative
Ich verletze **mir** oft die Hand.	dative (die Hand, a direct object)
Wann wäschst du **dich**?	accusative
Wann wäschst du **dir** die Haare?	dative (die Haare, a direct object)

Like any other verb, a reflexive verb can be used in any tense.

Ich habe **mir** das Bein gebrochen.
Der David, hat er **sich** etwas (das Bein) gebrochen?

The following is a summary of the reflexive accusative and dative pronouns.

		Accusative			Dative	
Pronoun	Verb	Reflex. Pronoun	Pronoun	Verb	Ref. Pron.	Dir.Object
Ich	wasche	mich.	Ich	wasche	mir	die Hände.
Du	wäschst	dich.	Du	wäschst	dir	die Hände.
Er	wäscht	**sich.**	Er	wäscht	**sich**	die Hände.
Sie	wäscht	**sich.**	Sie	wäscht	**sich**	die Hände.
Es	wäscht	**sich.**	Es	wäscht	**sich**	die Hände.
Wir	waschen	uns.	Wir	waschen	uns	die Hände.
Ihr	wascht	euch.	Ihr	wascht	euch	die Hände.
Sie	waschen	**sich.**	Sie	waschen	sich	die Hände.

A. Underline all reflexive pronouns in the accusative case and circle all reflexive pronouns in the dative case.

1. Habt ihr euch verletzt, oder habt ihr (euch) etwas gebrochen?
2. Hast du dich gewaschen, oder hast du dir nur die Füße gewaschen?
3. Er hat sich zuerst die Haare gewaschen, und dann hat er sich gewaschen.
4. Ich hab mich schwer verletzt; ich glaub, ich hab mir den Rücken verletzt.
5. Hast du dich verletzt, oder hast du dir sogar den Knöchel gebrochen?
6. Sie hat sich nichts gebrochen, sie hat sich nur verletzt.
7. Wir haben uns nicht wohl gefühlt, denn wir haben uns den Knöchel verstaucht.
8. Er wäscht sich jeden Tag, aber heute hat er sich auch die Haare gewaschen.
9. Hast du dich nur verletzt, oder hast du dir etwas gebrochen?

B. Fill in each blank with the correct reflexive pronoun.

1. Ich hab **mich** gestern beim Tennisspielen verletzt.
2. Hast du ________________ vielleicht etwas gebrochen?
3. Ich habe Glück gehabt, ich hab ________________ nicht verletzt.
4. Aber vor sieben Monaten hab ich ________________ den Daumen gebrochen.
5. Wann hat ________________ Peter verletzt?
6. Peter hat ________________ beim Rugbyspielen verletzt.
7. Wann hast du ________________ das letzte Mal gewaschen?
8. Ich hab ________________ gestern Abend die Haare gewaschen.
9. Meine Klassenkameraden haben ________________ nicht verletzt.
10. Wann habt ihr ________________ denn die Füße verletzt?

C. Write the following sentences in German, using the present perfect tense. Use the reflexive verb given in parentheses.

(s. verletzen)

1. I hurt myself. **Ich habe mich verletzt.**
2. I hurt my leg. **Ich habe mir das Bein verletzt.**

(s. kämmen)

3. She combed herself. ________________
4. She combed her hair. ________________

(s. waschen)

5. We washed ourselves. ________________
6. We washed our hands. ________________

(s. verletzen)

7. Did you hurt yourself? ________________
8. Did you hurt your foot? ________________

D. Summarize what you have learned about reflexive verbs and the use of reflexive pronouns.

____

____

____

DATIVE CASE INSTEAD OF FÜR + ACCUSATIVE

Pupil's Edition, p. 169

Compare In English as well as in German, you can use *"for* + an object" to express an opinion or concern.

That is too expensive **for me**. Das ist zu teuer **für mich**.
The car is too expensive **for my father**. Das Auto ist zu teuer **für meinen Vater**.

The **für + accusative** in the German sentences above can also be expressed by using the **dative case** instead.

FÜR + ACCUSATIVE	DATIVE
Das ist zu teuer **für mich**.	Das ist **mir** zu teuer.
Das Auto ist zu teuer **für meinen Vater**.	Das Auto ist **meinem Vater** zu teuer.

A. What case form should go into the blank? Accusative or dative? Check the appropriate column, then write either **mich** or **mir** in the blank.

	ACCUSATIVE	DATIVE
1. Das Shampoo ist für __mich__ nicht gut genug.	✓	_____
2. Die Sonnencreme ist __________ viel zu teuer.	_____	_____
3. Die Zahnpasta ist zu süß für __________ .	_____	_____
4. Die Handcreme ist __________ zu fett.	_____	_____
5. Diese Jacke ist __________ viel zu klein.	_____	_____
6. Dieses Hemd ist für __________ zu groß.	_____	_____
7. Dieser Gürtel ist __________ zu lang.	_____	_____
8. Der Berg ist zu steil für __________ .	_____	_____
9. Der Berg ist __________ zu steil.	_____	_____

B. Fill in each blank with the correct personal pronoun that matches the person being addressed.

1. Bobby! Diese Hose ist ______dir______ viel zu eng.
2. Herr Markquark! Diese Buch ist ____________________ zu langweilig.
3. Ach, Kinder! Dieser Film ist ____________________ bestimmt zu traurig.
4. Peter! Dieser Tennisschläger ist ____________________ viel zu teuer.
5. Aber Oma! Ist ____________________ dieser Kuchen nicht zu süß?
6. Mutti! Ich weiß, dass diese Beeren ____________________ zu sauer sind.
7. Connie! Diese Sojasprossen sind ____________________ wohl nicht frisch genug.

KAPITEL 6

C. Rewrite the following sentences, using dative case forms. Pay attention to the positon of the dative form in the sentence.

1. Dieser Anzug ist viel zu teuer für mich. **Dieser Anzug ist mir viel zu teuer.**
2. Das Rad ist zu klein für meine Schwester. ______________________
3. Die Sonnencreme ist zu teuer für ihn. ______________________
4. Das Wasser ist zu kalt für sie. ______________________
5. Die Pause ist für uns viel zu kurz. ______________________
6. Das Wetter ist zu schlecht für meinen Freund. ______________________
7. Die Erkältung dauert zu lange für mich. ______________________
8. Der Pulli ist für meinen Opa nicht warm genug. ______________________

D. Write the following sentences in German, using a dative pronoun.

1. The shirt is too big for me. **Das Hemd ist mir zu groß.**
2. The blouse is too expensive for her. ______________________
3. The belt is too short for him. ______________________
4. The coffee is too sweet for her. ______________________
5. The water is too cold for us. ______________________
6. The lotion is too greasy for them. ______________________
7. Dan, the weather is too bad for you! ______________________
8. Mr. K., the soup is too hot for you! ______________________

E. Summarize what you have learned about using the dative case instead of the preposition **für** and the accusative case.

____

____

KAPITEL 7

COMPARISON

Pupil's Edition, p. 190

In English **Comparison** refers to the inflection (change) of an adjective or adverb in order to show its relative intensity. The three degrees of comparison are **positive**, **comparative**, and **superlative**.

Look at the comparative and superlative forms of the following four adjectives. How are comparatives and superlatives formed in English?

POSITIVE	COMPARATIVE	SUPERLATIVE
small	smaller	smallest
beautiful	more beautiful	most beautiful
good	better	best

A. Read the following sentences. Underline all adjectives and determine the degree of comparison by checking the appropriate column.

	COMPARATIVE	SUPERLATIVE
1. My sister is older than Anna's sister.	✓	____
2. She must be the oldest in the family.	____	____
3. Who is the tallest in your family?	____	____
4. Jack is. But I am taller than Brent.	____	____
5. Do you see better in these glasses?	____	____
6. I see the best in my contacts.	____	____

In German The comparative and the superlative forms are very similar to English. For the **comparative**, add **-er** to the adjective; for the **superlative**, add **-st** or **-est** to the adjective. One-syllable adjectives often add an umlaut.

POSITIVE	COMPARATIVE	SUPERLATIVE
klein	klein**er**	klein**st-**
alt	**ä**lt**er**	**ä**lt**est-**
groß	gr**ö**ß**er**	gr**ö**ß**t-**

As in English, there are also some irregular comparative and superlative forms.

gern	**lieber**	**liebst-**
gut	**besser**	**best-**
viel	**mehr**	**meist-**

To compare two things that are **equal**, the words **so . . . wie** *(as . . . as)* and the **positive** form are used.

Die Luft ist hier **so** gut **wie** auf dem Land.

To compare two things that are **not equal,** the **comparative** form and the word **als** *(than)* are used.

Die Luft ist hier **besser als** in der Großstadt.

KAPITEL 7

B. In what form are these adjectives? Underline each adjective, then check the appropriate column.

	POSITIVE	COMPARATIVE	SUPERLATIVE
1. Unsere Wohnung ist größer als Opas.	____	✓	____
2. Ja, das ist eine große Wohnung.	____	____	____
3. Wir haben die größte Wohnung im Haus.	____	____	____
4. Diese Medizin ist besser als diese da.	____	____	____
5. Du, das ist aber auch eine gute Medizin.	____	____	____
6. Ich glaube, das ist die beste Medizin.	____	____	____
7. Diese Umgebung ist viel schöner.	____	____	____
8. Wir haben auch eine schöne Umgebung.	____	____	____

C. Fill in each blank with the appropriate comparative form.

1. (billig) Die Wohnungen sind auf dem Lande **billiger** .
2. (gut) Die Luft ist auf dem Lande auch ________________ .
3. (gern) Ich spiele Fußball ________________ als Volleyball.
4. (viel) Mein Bruder hat ________________ gegessen als ich.
5. (schön) Die Erdbeeren waren ________________ als die Blaubeeren.
6. (groß) Aber die Blaubeeren waren ________________ als die Erdbeeren.
7. (jung) Bist du viel ________________ als deine Kusine?
8. (alt) Ich bin sogar drei Monate ________________ als sie.

D. Fill in the blanks with equal or unequal comparisons, using the cues given.

1. (unequal / groß) Hamburg ist **größer als** München.
2. (equal) / groß) Köln ist ________________________ Düsseldorf.
3. (equal / gut) Fisch schmeckt mir ________________________ Fleisch.
4. (unequal / gesund) Fisch ist ________________________ Fleisch.
5. (equal / alt) Robert ist ________________________ seine Kusine.
6. (unequal / alt) Aber ich bin ________________________ mein Cousin.
7. (unequal / jung) Ich bin aber ________________________ mein Bruder.
8. (equal / jung) Ich weiß, du bist ________________________ meine Schwester.

E. How would you summarize what you have learned about comparisons?

____

____

ADJECTIVES

In English An **adjective** is a word that describes a noun or pronoun. An adjective tells *what kind, which one, how much,* or *how many.*

what kind:	This is a *beautiful* garden.
	The garden is *gorgeous*, and it is *large.*
which one:	It is the *largest* garden in the city.
how much:	There are *no* gardens here.
how many:	There are *many* gardens here.

A. Underline each adjective in the following sentences.

1. We live in a little village in the beautiful Alps.
2. We have a small house with a large garden.
3. The garden has many trees and gorgeous flowers in the spring.
4. We also have a modern pool and a large grill in our backyard.
5. Grandma enjoys the old-fashioned kitchen and the cozy living room.
6. I have a large bedroom with a sunny terrace. It is beautiful!

In German **Adjectives** have endings in German when they are used before a noun. In this section, adjectives preceded by **ein, kein, mein,** etc., are discussed.

Wir haben einen groß**en** Garten. Ein groß**er** Garten ist praktisch.

When an adjective modifies a noun that is used with an **ein-** word – the indefinite article or a possessive – the adjective must show the gender of the noun, because the word **ein** does not clearly show gender. The ending **-er** on groß**er** Garten tells you that Garten is a masculine noun, and the ending **-es** on klein**es** Zimmer tells you that Zimmer is a neuter noun.

MASCULINE	FEMININE	NEUTER
Das ist: ein groß**er** Garten.	ein**e** sonnig**e** Terrasse.	ein klein**es** Zimmer.
Wir haben: ein**en** groß**en** Garten.	ein**e** sonnig**e** Terrasse.	ein klein**es** Zimmer.
Das ist: mein klein**er** Hund.	mein**e** klein**e** Katze.	mein klein**es** Zimmer.
Wo hast du: dein**en** klein**en** Hund?	dein**e** klein**e** Katze?	dein klein**es** Zimmer?

KAPITEL 7

B. Underline each adjective in the following sentences.

1. Wir wohnen in einem <u>kleinen</u> Dorf in den <u>schönen</u> Alpen.
2. Wir haben ein schönes Haus mit einem großen Garten.
3. Im Garten stehen alte Bäume, und im Frühling haben wir wunderschöne Blumen.
4. Wir haben auch einen ganz modernen Pool und einen großen Grill im Garten.
5. Oma hat eine altmodische Küche und ein gemütliches Wohnzimmer.
6. Ich habe ein großes Schlafzimmer und eine sonnige Terrasse.

C. In the following sentences, you may not know the meaning of every noun. However, you can determine what gender they are. Check the appropriate column.

	MASCULINE	FEMININE	NEUTER
1. Diese Jeans ist sehr modisch.	_____	✓	_____
2. Ein blauer Smoking steht dir gut.	_____	_____	_____
3. Eine weiße Fliege dazu sieht gut aus.	_____	_____	_____
4. Ein ruhiger Flug tut mir immer gut.	_____	_____	_____
5. Wo wir sind, da gibt es eine kleine Bucht.	_____	_____	_____
6. Ein weißer Strand lädt uns ein.	_____	_____	_____
7. Schau, da springt ein grüner Frosch!	_____	_____	_____
8. Sieh! Da ist auch ein kleines Meerschweinchen.	_____	_____	_____
9. Und da ist auch eine kleine Schildkröte!	_____	_____	_____
10. Da ist ein neuer Bildschirm für dich.	_____	_____	_____
11. Und hier ist ein neues Schlüsselwort.	_____	_____	_____
12. Und da ist auch eine neue Maus für dich.	_____	_____	_____

D. Summarize what you have learned about German adjectives and their endings before **ein**-words.

____

____

ADJECTIVE ENDINGS FOLLOWING EIN-WORDS

Pupil's Edition, p. 194

In German Adjectives have special endings. These endings depend upon the **gender** (masculine, feminine, neuter), **number** (singular, plural), and **case** (nominative, accusative, dative, genitive) of the noun they describe or modify, and also upon whether they are preceded by a **definite article** or other **der**-words (**dieser, jeder, welcher**), or by an **indefinite article** or other **ein**-words (**kein** and the possessives).

1. In the nominative case and accusative case, adjectives have these endings:

	Nominative			Accusative		
Masculine	Das ist ein	groß **er**	Garten.	Wir haben einen	groß **en**	Garten.
Feminine	Das ist eine	groß **e**	Küche.	Wir haben eine	groß **e**	Küche.
Neuter	Das ist ein	groß **es**	Zimmer.	Wir haben ein	groß **es**	Zimmer.
Plural	Das sind	groß **e**	Häuser.	Wir haben	groß **e**	Häuser.

2. In the dative case, all adjectives have the ending **-en** for nouns of all gender and number.

	Dative		
Masculine	Wir sitzen in einem	groß **en**	Garten.
Feminine	Wir sitzen in einer	groß **en**	Küche.
Neuter	Wir sitzen in einem	groß **en**	Zimmer.
Plural	Wir leben in	groß **en**	Städten.

3. When more than one adjective modifies a noun, they all have the same ending.

   Wir haben ein schön **es**, groß **es** und gemütlich **es** Wohnzimmer.

4. Numerals are plurals and have the plural ending **-e** for nominative and accusative, and **-en** for the dative.

Nominative	Das sind zwei schön **e** Zimmer.
Accusative	Wir haben drei groß **e** Badezimmer.
Dative	Ich habe in vier klein **en** Städten gewohnt.

A. Fill in each blank with the correct adjective ending.

1. Wir haben ein klein__es__ Haus in einer groß__en__ Stadt.
2. Unser klein_____ Haus hat vier groß_____ Zimmer und einen klein_____ Keller.
3. Mutti hat eine modern_____ Küche, und ich habe mein eigen_____ Zimmer.
4. Vati hat sein eigen_____ Computerzimmer, wo er seinen neu_____ Computer hat.
5. Wir haben einen klein_____ Garten und eine klein_____ Terrasse.
6. Wir sitzen gern in unserem klein_____ Garten oder auf unserer klein_____ Terrasse.
7. Sag, hast du dein eigen_____ Zimmer, wo jetzt dein neu_____ Computer steht?
8. Bei uns haben alle ihr eigen_____ Zimmer, und Mutti hat ihren eigen_____ Garten.
9. In ihrem schön_____ Garten wachsen schöne bunt_____ Blumen.

10. Wir haben leider keinen groß_____ Pool in unserm schön_____ Garten.

11. Ich möchte einen gut_____ Job und ein gut_____ Einkommen haben.

12. Ich will ein friedlich_____ Leben haben und in einer sauber_____ Umwelt wohnen.

B. Now fill in each blank with the correct form of the adjective in parentheses.

1. (neu) Eine **neue** Wohnung kostet mehr Geld.
2. (gemütlich) Ein ______________________ Garten ist immer sehr schön.
3. (eigen) Ein ______________________ Zimmer ist etwas Schönes für mich.
4. (groß) Ein ______________________ Badezimmer ist im 2. Stock.
5. (kühl) Ein ______________________ Keller ist gut für Vatis Wein.
6. (klein) Ein ______________________ Pool ist auch im Garten.
7. (ruhig) Eine ______________________ Terrasse ist gut für Mutti.
8. (neu) Ein ______________________ Computer steht in meinem Zimmer.
9. (friedlich) Ja, wir lieben ein ______________________ Leben.
10. (sauber) Wir lieben eine ______________________ Umwelt.
11. (sicher) Wir haben ein ______________________ Einkommen.
12. (eigen) Und ich wünsche mir ein ______________________ Auto!

C. Fill in each blank with the correct form of the words given in parentheses.

1. (ein / grün) Ich brauche **einen grünen** Pullover.
2. (mein / rot) Hast du ______________________ Hemd gesehen?
3. (ihr / weiß) ______________________ T-Shirt gefällt mir aber nicht.
4. (unser / braun) Gefällt dir ______________________ Teppich?
5. (sein / alt) Er hat ______________________ Opa Pralinen geschenkt.
6. (dein / nett) Ich möchte gern ______________________ Schwester ins Kino einladen.
7. (euer / neu) Was habt ihr mit ______________________ Auto gemacht?
8. (kein / gut) Zur Zeit läuft ______________________ Film im Kino.
9. (ein / spannend) Ich möchte mal wieder ______________________ Film sehen.
10. (zwei / toll) Wir haben letzte Woche ______________________ Filme gesehen.

D. Summarize what you have learned about endings of adjectives following **ein-** words.

____

____

____

KAPITEL 8

ADJECTIVE ENDINGS FOLLOWING DER AND DIESER-WORDS

Pupil's Edition, p. 217

In German Adjectives following **der** and **dieser**-words (**dieser, jeder, welcher**) have different endings from adjectives following **ein**-words.

1. In the nominative case and accusative case, adjectives have these endings:

	Nominative	Accusative
Masculine	Der groß**e** Garten gefällt mir.	Ich liebe diesen groß**en** Garten.
Feminine	Die groß**e** Küche gefällt mir.	Ich liebe diese groß**e** Küche.
Neuter	Das groß**e** Zimmer gefällt mir.	Ich liebe dieses groß**e** Zimmer.
Plural	Die groß**en** Häuser gefallen mir.	Ich liebe diese groß**en** Häuser.

2. In the dative case, all adjectives have the ending **-en** for nouns of all gender and number.

	Dative
Masculine	Wir sitzen gern in diesem groß**en** Garten.
Feminine	Wir kochen gern in dieser groß**en** Küche.
Neuter	Ich schlafe gern in diesem groß**en** Zimmer.
Plural	Wir leben gern in diesen groß**en** Häusern.

3. When two or more adjectives modify a noun, they all have the same ending.

   Wir sitzen gern in diesem schön**en**, groß**en** Garten.

A. Fill in each blank with the correct adjective ending.

1. Dieses alt__e__ Haus steht in diesem schön__en__ Garten.
2. Diese schön____ Blumen wachsen in diesem groß____ Garten.
3. Diese neu____ Gartenmöbel sind zu groß für diese klein____ Terrasse.
4. Mir gefällt dieser grün____ Stuhl und diese alt____ Couch.
5. Wo hast du denn dieses toll____ Bild und diesen alt____ Teppich gekauft?
6. Du, mir gefällt diese schwarz____ Jacke und dieses grau____ Hemd.
7. Wo hast du denn diese alt____ Klamotten gekauft? In diesem billig___ Geschäft?
8. Diese schwarz____ Fliege passt gut zu diesem weiß____ Hemd.
9. Dieses witzig____ T-Shirt gefällt mir gut, aber diese bunt____ Hose gefällt mir nicht.
10. Diese blau____ Socken passen nicht zu den braun____ Schuhen.
11. Warum willst du diese schön____ , weiß____ Bluse wegwerfen?
12. Diese schwarz____ Jeans und das bunt____ Shirt darüber sieht echt cool aus.

B. Fill in each blank with the correct form of the words given in parentheses.

1. (das / blau) Warum ziehst du nicht **das blaue** Hemd an?
2. (dieser / grün) Ich mag ____________ Anorak nicht.
3. (dieses / bunt) ____________ Hemd kostet nur d 6.50!
4. (dieser/ schick) Wo hast du denn ____________ Hut gekauft?
5. (dieser / weiß) Du siehst einfach toll aus in ____________ Bluse.
6. (welche / gelb) ____________ Socken willst du anziehen?
7. (welch / klein) Ich weiß in ____________ Stadt ich das gesehen habe.
8. (die / olivgrün) Mir gefällt ____________ Jacke nicht.
9. (der / türkisblau) Zieh doch mal ____________ Pulli an!
10. (diese / braun) Wo hast du ____________ Schuhe gekauft?
11. (diese / alt) In ____________ Schuhen kann ich nicht laufen.
12. (der / schwarz) Ich möchte heute ____________ Blazer anziehen.

C. Summarize what you have learned about adjective endings for adjectives following **der** and **dieser**-words.

____

____

____

KAPITEL 9

PREPOSITIONS

Pupil's Edition, p. 246

In English A **preposition** is a word that shows the relationship between a noun or pronoun and another word in the sentence. Prepositions may indicate position, direction, or time.

Let's drive **to** Los Angeles.	We can go **in** August.
But don't go **without** us.	We would like to ride **with** you.
I am **from** Brandenburg.	I'll see you **on** your birthday.

The noun or pronoun that the preposition connects to the rest of the sentence is called the **object of the preposition**. The preposition and its object together are called a **prepositional phrase**.

A. In each of the following sentences, underline the prepositional phrases and circle the prepositions.

1. We are driving (to) Munich, and we will stay (in) this city (for) three weeks.
2. I want to go on a boat ride down the Isar.
3. We might also go hiking in the mountains near Salzburg.
4. If the weather is bad, we could visit the cathedral instead of the mountains.
5. According to the guidebook, the pass is closed in the winter months.
6. The weather in Munich is warm in the summer, even after dark.
7. Among other things, we will eat at the Hofbräuhaus for a taste of the local cuisine.

In German **All prepositions take objects in a particular case**: accusative, dative, or genitive.

Accusative case	Dieser Pulli ist **für meinen Bruder**.
	Und dieser Pulli da ist **für mich**.
Dative case	Michael kommt **mit dem Rad**.
	Diese Kirche ist **aus dem vierzehnten Jahrhundert**.

German also has a group of prepositions called **two-way prepositions**. The two-way prepositions are **an, auf, in, hinter, vor, unter, über, neben**, and **zwischen**. The objects of these prepositions can be either in the accusative case or in the dative case.

a. The objects of the prepositions are in the **accusative case** when they are used with a verb that indicates **direction**.
Wir fahren **an die Ostsee auf die Insel Rügen**.

b. The objects of the prepositions are in the **dative case** when they are used with a verb that indicates **location**.
Wir waren **an der Ostsee auf der Insel Rügen**.

c. Certain prepositions combine with the definite articles **das** and **dem** to spell one word.

combinations with **das**	(direction)	combinations with **dem**	(location)
an + das	= **ans**	an + dem	= **am**
in + das	= **ins**	in + dem	= **im**
vor + das	= **vors**	vor + dem	= **vorm**
unter + das	= **unters**	unter + dem	= **unterm**
über + das	= **übers**	über + dem	= **überm**
hinter + das	= **hinters**	hinter + dem	= **hinterm**

B. In each of the following sentences, circle the prepositions und underline the prepositional phrases.

1. Die Kinder spielen mit ihren Bällen auf dem Schulhof.
2. Hinter dem Haus steht das Fahrrad von meinem Bruder.
3. Diese Platte aus den 70er Jahren ist für meine Großmutter.
4. Ein Schüler geht in das Klassenzimmer und schreibt „Ruhe!“ an die Tafel.
5. In diesem Dorf gibt es eine Kirche aus dem 15. Jahrhundert.
6. Wenn du durch das Stadttor gehst, kommst du in die alte Innenstadt.
7. Unser Auto steht auf dem Parkplatz in der Fräuleinstraße.
8. Ich warte vor dem eleganten Café neben dem alten Rathaus.
9. Wir fahren nach Garmisch und von dort aus steigen wir auf die Zugspitze.
10. Ich war mit meinen Freunden eine Woche in den Bergen.

C. In the following sentences, do the prepositional phrases indicate direction or location? Check the appropriate column.

	LOCATION	DIRECTION
1. Wir waren eine Woche in den Bergen.	✓	______
2. Nächstes Jahr fahren wir an die Nordsee.	______	______
3. Warst du schon mal an der Nordsee?	______	______
4. Ich bin noch nie am Bodensee gewesen.	______	______
5. Wann gehst du auf den Tennisplatz?	______	______
6. Geh rein ins Haus!	______	______
7. Wir waren den ganzen Tag in der Stadt.	______	______
8. Fahr das Auto hinters Haus!	______	______
9. Hinterm Haus haben wir die Garage.	______	______

D. Summarize what you have learned about prepositions that can be followed by either the accusative case or the dative case.

____

DATIVE PREPOSITIONS

Pupil's Edition, p. 254

In German The following prepositions, **aus, bei, mit, nach, von, zu, seit, gegenüber,** always take an object in the **dative case**.

1. Read the following sentences and notice the meanings and use of these prepositions.

aus *from, out of*	Dieses Haus ist **aus dem 16. Jahrhundert.**
bei *at, by, near*	Ich bin **bei meiner Tante.** Sie wohnt **bei der Schule.**
mit *with*	Wir kommen heute **mit dem Bus.**
nach *after*	Was machst du **nach der Schule?**
von *from*	Der Pulli ist **von meiner Oma.**
zu *to*	Wann gehst du **zur Post** und wann **zum Bäcker?**
seit *since*	Dieses Tor steht **seit dem 15. Jahrhundert.**
gegenüber *across from*	Wir wohnen **gegenüber der Schule.**

2. The prepositions **bei** and **zu** combined with the definite article **dem** are spelled as one word.

   bei + dem = **beim**　　　　zu + dem = **zum**

A. In the following sentences, underline the prepositional phrases and circle the prepositions.

1. Fährst du heute mit dem Rad zur Schule?
2. Ich war zuerst beim Metzger, und jetzt gehe ich zum Bäcker.
3. Nach dem Kino gehe ich mit meinen Freunden ein Eis essen.
4. Dieses T-Shirt ist von meiner Oma und dieses Stirnband von meinem Opa.
5. Seit der Pause habe ich mit meinem Mathelehrer gesprochen.
6. Der Rolf kommt eben aus dem Buchladen neben der Schule.
7. Bei uns gibt es heute einen Kuchen von meiner Tante.
8. Nach der Fete kommen meine Freunde zu mir.
9. Wann gehst du denn mit mir zur Post?
10. Ich warte bei der Schule gegenüber der Post.
11. Seit meinem vierzehnten Geburtstag gehe ich einmal im Jahr zum Arzt.
12. Zu welcher Zeit kannst du mit deinen Geschwistern zu uns kommen?

B. Fill in each blank with an appropriate dative preposition.

1. Ich gehe ___mit___ meinem Freund ___nach___ der Schule ins Kino.
2. Und ______________ dem Kino gehen wir zusammen ______________ einem Freund.
3. Diese Schuhe habe ich ______________ meinem großen Bruder.
4. Ich kenne unseren Biolehrer ______________ der dritten Klasse.
5. Die Kirche ist doch *(across from)* ______________ dem Rathaus.
6. Der Bäcker ist doch gleich ______________ dem Metzger.
7. Weil es so heiß ist, gehe ich fast nie ______________ dem Haus.
8. Zuerst kommt der Bäcker und ______________ etwa 30 Metern kommt der Obstladen.
9. Fährst du ______________ dem Tennisspiel ______________ mir in die Stadt?
10. Ich esse heute ______________ den Großeltern, weil die Mutti ______________ Vati weg ist.

C. Fill in each blank with the correct form of the definite article.

1. Heute kommen aber viele Leute aus ___dem___ Kino.
2. Ich hol dich nach ______________ Schule mit ______________ Moped ab.
3. Von ______________ Post bis zu ______________ Tennisplätzen sind es fünf Minuten.
4. Bei ______________ Tante Rosa gibt es heute etwas Gutes zu essen.
5. Wer steigt denn da aus ______________ Auto?
6. Wer ist der Mann mit __________ dunklen Regenmantel und __________ braunen Tasche?
7. Ich habe unsern Englischlehrer seit ______________ Englischunterricht nicht mehr gesehen.

D. Fill in each blank with the correct form of the word given in parentheses.

1. (mein) Ich war mit ___meinen___ Geschwistern bei ___meinen___ Großeltern.
2. (unser) Da kommt ja der Basti mit ______________ Hund aus ______________ Garage.
3. (dein) Seit ______________ Geburtstag war ich nicht mehr bei ______________ Oma.
4. (ihr) Da kommt die Erika mit ______________ Mutter und ______________ Bruder.
5. (sein) Ich warte mit ______________ Freunden gegenüber ______________ Haus.
6. (unser) Bei ______________ Bäcker und bei ______________ Metzger ist alles frisch!
7. (unser) Von ______________ Haus bis zu ______________ Schule sind es 2 Kilometer.

E. Summarize what you have learned about prepositions such as **aus, bei, mit**, etc.

____

____

KAPITEL 9

ACCUSATIVE PREPOSITIONS

Pupil's Edition, p. 254

In German The following prepositions, **durch, für, gegen, ohne, um,** always take an object in the **accusative case**.

1. Read the following sentences and notice the meanings and use of these prepositions.

durch *through*	Wir gehen gleich **durch das Stadttor.**
für *for*	Ich spiele Fußball **für unsere Schule.**
gegen *against*	Wir spielen **gegen eine gute Mannschaft.**
ohne *without*	Wir spielen **ohne unseren besten Spieler, den Rolf.**
um *around*	Die Schule ist gleich hier **um die Ecke.**

2. The prepositions **durch, für, um** combine with the definite article **das** and are spelled as one word.

durch + das = **durchs** für + das = **fürs** um + das = **ums**

A. Fill in each blank with an appropriate accusative preposition.

1. Ist dieses Geschenk ____**für**____ deine Freundin?
2. Die Schüler laufen ________________ den Tennisplatz.
3. Ich weiß einen kürzeren Weg; gehen wir ________________ den Stadtpark.
4. Was ist los? Du kommst ________________ deinen Rucksack zur Schule?
5. Mein Bruder ist mit dem Auto ________________ die Garagentür gefahren.
6. Komm ja nicht ________________ Obst und Gemüse nach Hause!
7. Was hast du eigentlich ________________ mich zum Essen?
8. Du hast ja deine Freundin ________________ mich kennen gelernt.
9. Du kannst deine Hausaufgaben heute mal ________________ mich machen.

B. Fill in each blank with an appropriate definite article or possessive.

1. Ich bin ohne **meine** Freundin um **den** Bodensee gefahren.
2. Ich habe den Jens durch ________ guten Freund kennen gelernt.
3. Dieses Handy habe ich für ________ Oma und für ________ Opa gekauft.
4. Was hast du denn für ________ Vater zum Geburtstag gekauft?
5. Ich habe eine gute Medizin gegen ________ Husten.
6. Wir haben nichts gegen ________ neue Schülerin.
7. Ich gehe nicht ohne ________ Regenmantel aus dem Haus.
8. Wir fahren nicht gern durch ________ dunklen Wald.
9. Ich glaube, die Post ist hier gleich um ________ Ecke.

C. Fill in each blank with the correct form of the definite article. Use contractions where appropriate.

1. Der Junge läuft aus **dem** Haus und durch **den** Garten.
2. Nach ________ Schule gehen wir ohne ________ Lehrer zum Fußballspielen.
3. Wir joggen durch ________ Rathaus und um ________ Park.
4. Wir fahren morgen mit ________ Eltern an ________ Ostsee.
5. Sie waren seit ________ Krieg nicht mehr an ________ Ostsee.
6. Wir joggen um ________ See und dann *(through)* ________ Dorf.
7. Ich gehe jetzt mit ________ Kindern in ________ Fitnessraum.
8. Die Tür *(to)* ________ Fitnessraum ist gegenüber ________ Sauna.
9. Neben ________ Schule und gegenüber ________ Kirche ist die Bücherei.
10. Gehst du in ______ Telefonzelle oder kommst du aus ________ Telefonzelle?
11. Ich gehe mit ________ Oma *(to)* ________ Bäcker gegenüber ________ Post.
12. Ich habe nichts von ________ Arzt und von ________ Ärztin gelesen!

D. Summarize what you have learned about the various uses of German prepositions.

____

____

KAPITEL 10

PREPOSITIONS USED WITH VERBS AND ADJECTIVES

Pupil's Edition, p. 277

Compare You have learned certain meanings for each preposition.

auf: auf dem Tisch *on: on the table* **in**: in der Stadt *in: in the city*

a. Prepositions can also be used with verbs in fixed combinations, and the meaning conveyed by the preposition varies from expression to expression. Look at these prepositions and note their different meanings.

auf: warten **auf** = to wait ***for*** s. freuen **auf** = to look forward ***to***
für: s. interessieren **für** = to be interested ***in***
an: kein Interesse haben **an** = to have no interest ***in***
zu: passen **zu** = to go ***with***
über: sprechen **über** = to talk ***about***

b. There are also adjectives used with prepositions in fixed combinations.

mit: verheiratet **mit** = married ***to*** zufrieden **mit** = satisfied ***with***
gegen: allergisch **gegen** = allergic ***to***

c. You must learn the verb phrases and adjectives by heart and learn what case is used with each one.

warten auf (acc.)	s. freuen auf (acc.)	s. interessieren für (acc.)
sprechen über (acc.)	Interesse haben an (dat.)	passen zu (dat.)
verheiratet mit (dat.)	zufrieden mit (dat.)	allergisch gegen (acc.)

d. Sometimes English uses a preposition with a verb and German does not, or the other way around.

to look ***for*** suchen antworten **auf** to answer

A. In the following sentences, fill in each blank with the correct preposition.

1. Interessierst du dich **für** Computertechnologie?
2. Wir haben kein Interesse ________ Mode.
3. Ich höre, du bist allergisch ________ Erdbeeren und Bananen.
4. Meine Oma freut sich sehr ________ unseren Besuch in den Ferien.
5. Ich habe gestern mit ihr ________ unseren Besuch gesprochen.
6. Sie sagt, sie wartet ________ eine E-Mail von uns.
7. Ich werde ________ ihre E-Mail sofort antworten.
8. Bist du zufrieden ________ deiner Deutscharbeit?

B. Fill in each blank with the correct form of the possessive given in parentheses.

1. (dein) Ich interessiere mich nicht für **deine** alten Klamotten.
2. (ihr) Wir freuen uns über ____________ Besuch zu Ostern.
3. (sein) Ich warte schon seit drei Wochen auf ____________ Brief.
4. (unser) Hast du schon über ____________ Besuch in den USA gesprochen?
5. (mein) Warum antwortest du nicht auf ____________ Frage?
6. (dein) Ich habe kein Interesse an ____________ Videokamera.
7. (ihr) Aber ich interessiere mich für ____________ Fernseher.
8. (dein) Ich bin allergisch gegen ____________ Blumen.

C. Write the following sentences in German.

1. I have no interest in his camera. **Ich habe kein Interesse an seiner Kamera.**
2. Are you interested in his camera? ____________
3. She is allergic to fruit. ____________
4. I'm looking for a dog. ____________
5. I'm looking forward to my vacation. ____________
6. We are waiting for the bus. ____________
7. For whom are you waiting? ____________
8. He is married to my aunt. ____________
9. This shirt goes well with your pants. ____________
10. I am satisfied with your grades. ____________

D. Summarize what you have learned about verbs and adjectives that are used with certain prepositions.

____

____

NOUN OBJECTS OF A PREPOSITION: DA-COMPOUNDS AND WO-COMPOUNDS

Pupil's Edition, p. 277

In English You can replace the **noun object of a preposition** with an object pronoun. The object pronoun can replace a person or a thing.

	NOUN OBJECT		PRONOUN OBJECT
Mark talks about	*his best friend John.*	Mark talks about	*him.*
Mark talks about	*the latest movie.*	Mark talks about	*it.*

A. Replace the noun object of the preposition in the first sentence with an object pronoun in the second sentence.

1. We're talking about the weather report. We're talking about ___it___ .
2. How much will you take for that vase? How much will you take for __________ ?
3. Roberta is interested in horses. Roberta is interested in __________ .
4. Did you give the card to Mrs. Hill? Did you give the card to __________ ?
5. It was nice of you to clean up after Bob and Dan.

   It was nice of you to clean up after __________ .

In German You can replace the **noun object of a preposition** with an object pronoun only if the noun refers to a person. A **da**-compound is used when the noun refers to a thing. A **da**-compound is the preposition preceded by the prefix **da-**.

	NOUN OBJECT		PRONOUN OBJECT	
Mark spricht über	*seinen Freund Johan.*	Mark spricht über	*ihn.*	(person)
Mark spricht über	*den letzten Film.*	Mark spricht	**darüber**.	(thing)

When asking questions, you can use the interrogative **wen** after the preposition only if it refers to a person. In more formal German, a **wo**-compound (**wo-** + preposition) is used when you refer to a thing. In colloquial German, the **preposition + was** is most often used.

	NOUN OBJECT	INTERROGATIVE	
Mark spricht über	*seinen Freund Johan.*	**Über wen** spricht Mark?	(person)
Mark spricht über	*den letzten Film.*	**Worüber** spricht Mark?	(thing)
Mark spricht über	*den letzten Film.*	**Über was** spricht Mark?	(thing, colloquial)

Note: If a preposition begins with a vowel, an *r* is inserted between **wo** and **da** to facilitate pronunciation.

für: **da**für, **wo**für   auf: **dar**auf, **wor**auf   über: **dar**über, **wor**über

B. Underline the prepositional phrase in the first sentence, then fill in each blank with either a pronoun or a **da-**compound.

1. Wir sprechen über das Spiel. Sprecht ihr auch **darüber** ?
2. Wir sprechen über unseren Präsidenten. Sprecht ihr auch ________________ ?
3. Ich interessiere mich für Politik. Interessierst du dich auch ________________ ?
4. Ich spreche gern über diese Schauspielerin. Sprichst du auch gern ________________ ?
5. Freust du dich auf die Ferien? Ich freue mich schon sehr ________________ .
6. Meine Großeltern kommen aus Deutschland, und wir freuen uns ________________ .

C. Determine if the statement that refers to something is a more formal or a more colloquial statement. Check the appropriate column.

	FORMAL	COLLOQUIAL
1. Ich weiß nicht, worüber er sich so freut.	✓	____
2. Ich weiß, über was er heute spricht.	____	____
3. Für was interessierst du dich eigentlich?	____	____
4. Und wofür interessiert sich deine Freundin?	____	____
5. Worauf freut ihr euch?	____	____
6. Ich kann mir denken, auf was ihr euch freut.	____	____

D. Fill in the blanks with either a **wo-**compound or a preposition and **was**, depending on the situation.

1. **Worüber** sprichst du denn, Ulf? Über den Film gestern Abend?
2. Herr Müller, ________________ sprechen Sie heute in der Klasse? Über Politik?
3. ________________ interessieren Sie sich denn am meisten, Frau Hinterholzer?
4. Für Briefmarken? ________________ interessierst du dich denn noch, Sina?
5. Sag mir, Jack, ________________ freust du dich denn am meisten? Auf Ostern?
6. Herr Seegruber, ________________ freuen Sie sich denn am meisten?
7. ________________ diskutiert ihr nicht gern, Anja und Karla? Über Sport?
8. ________________ diskutieren Sie heute im Fernsehen, Herr Weißmüller?

E. Summarize what you have learned about **da-**compounds and **wo-**compounds.

____

____

FUTURE TENSE

Pupil's Edition, p. 289

In English The **future tense** is used to express an action that will take place sometime in the future. The future tense is formed by using the helping verb *will* and the infinitive of the main verb.

We	*will visit*	our grandparents on the weekend.
I	*will go*	to the movies tonight.

A. Rewrite these sentences in the future tense.

1. I am reading a book about Napoleon.
   I will read a book about Napoleon.
2. We are going to the movies.
   ______
3. Have you seen the Matterhorn?
   ______
4. They were in Berlin over the weekend.
   ______
5. Mr. Lewis has some papers for you.
   ______

In German The **future tense** is formed by using the helping verb **werden + the infinitive** of the main verb. The helping verb is conjugated for person and number, and as a conjugated verb is in second position. The infinitive of the main verb goes to the end of the sentence.

	HELPING VERB		INFINITIVE
Wir	**werden**	unsere Großeltern am Wochenende	**besuchen**.
Ich	**werde**	heute Abend ins Kino	**gehen**.

In dependent clauses, however, the conjugated verb goes to the end, after the infinitive.

	INFINITIVE	HELPING VERB
Ich denke, dass wir unsere Großeltern am Wochenende	**besuchen**	werden.
Ich weiß nicht, ob ich heute Abend ins Kino	**gehen**	werde.

In German, the construction **werden + infinitive** is far less used to express future time than its equivalent in English. German uses the present tense with an adverb indicating future time more than the future tense. Such adverbs can be words or expressions such as **morgen, nächsten Sonntag** etc.

Ich gehe **morgen** ins Kino. (present tense to express future time)

KAPITEL 10

B. Read the following sentences that refer to future time. Some sentences use the present tense to express future time, while others use the future tense. Check the correct column.

	Future Tense	Present Tense
1. Ich höre mir heute Abend den Wetterbericht an.	____	✓
2. Ich werde heute Abend nicht fernsehen.	____	____
3. Ich werde mir ein Auto mit Klimaanlage kaufen.	____	____
4. Ich kaufe mir am Wochenende einen neuen Fernseher.	____	____
5. Ich mache nächstes Jahr den Führerschein.	____	____
6. Ich werde bestimmt 1000 Euro dafür ausgeben.	____	____

C. Read the following sentences and fill in the blanks with the correct form of the verb **werden**.

1. Du **wirst** dir bestimmt einen Fernseher mit HD-Anschluss kaufen.
2. Ich ____________ mir nächsten Monat einen neuen Computer kaufen.
3. Wann ____________ sich der Martin ein neues Handy kaufen?
4. Wir ____________ uns zu Hause einen Laptop kaufen.
5. Wie lange ____________ ihr noch im Internet surfen?
6. Mathias ____________ wohl wieder mit seiner Cathy im Chatroom sprechen.

D. Rewrite the following sentences in the future tense.

1. Ich lese dieses Buch nicht.

   Ich werde dieses Buch nicht lesen.

2. Gehst du heute mit Anke ins Kino?

   ____

3. Anke hat keine Zeit.

   ____

4. Wann fliegt ihr denn nach Berlin?

   ____

5. Wir fliegen erst im April.

   ____

E. Summarize what you know about the use of the verb **werden**.

____

____

KAPITEL 11

POLITE REQUESTS (WÜRDE-FORMS)

Pupil's Edition, p. 307

In English The **conditional** has many uses. One of them is the conditional used **in expressions of wish involving the future** or in **polite requests**.

Wishes involving the future:

> **Would** you **like to go** to an Italian restaurant?
> We **would like to eat** in a Chinese restaurant again.

Polite requests:

> **Would** you take me to the ballet?

A. Rephrase these sentences as polite requests.

1. Take me out to the ball game. **Would you take me out to the ball game?**
2. Give me the book. ______________________
3. Bring chips to the party. ______________________
4. Pass the salt. ______________________
5. Can you sew this button on for me? ______________________
6. Will you come to see the play? ______________________
7. Turn off the TV. ______________________
8. Clean your room today. ______________________

KAPITEL 11

In German The **conditional** is used in German much the same way as in English. **In expressions of wish involving the future** and **in polite requests**, you use the **würde**-forms.

Wishes involving the future:

> **Würdest** du gern mit mir in ein italienisches Restaurant **gehen**?
> Wir **würden** gern in einem chinesischen Restaurant **essen**.

Polite Requests:

> **Würdest** du mich bitte ins Ballett **mitnehmen**?

The **würde**-forms are:

	Singular		Plural
ich	**würde**	wir	**würden**
du	**würdest**	ihr	**würdet**
er, sie, es	**würde**	sie, Sie	**würden**

B. Fill in each blank with the correct **würde-** form.

1. Ich **würde** gern mal geräucherten Fisch essen.
2. Was ______________ ihr gern mal essen?
3. Wir ______________ gern mal marinierten Lachs essen.
4. Was ______________ Sie denn gern mal essen, Frau Seidenfaden?
5. Ich weiß, dass Hannah gern mal frische Pilze essen ______________ .
6. Und du, Dannie, was ______________ du gern mal essen?
7. Die Kinder ______________ am liebsten nur Eis essen.
8. Was ______________ ihr denn am liebsten zur Brotzeit trinken?

C. Write each of the following sentences in German, using the correct **würde-** form and **gern**.

1. I would like to eat a salad. **Ich würde gern einen Salat essen.**
2. What would you like to eat, Thomas? ______________
3. Mark would like to eat a steak. ______________
4. Mr. Brown would like to eat fish. ______________
5. What would you like to eat, Ms. Bea? ______________
6. We would like to drink milk. ______________
7. Mia would like to go to the movies. ______________
8. Would you like to go swimming, Al? ______________
9. I would like to play tennis. ______________

D. Summarize what you have learned about making polite requests.

____

____

____

KAPITEL 11

UNPRECEDED ADJECTIVES

Pupil's Edition, p. 311

In English Adjectives can be preceded by an article or not. Read these sentences.

adjective preceded by a definite article: *The* **dark** bread tasted delicious.
adjective preceded by an indefinite article: *A* **dark** bread goes well with this cheese.
adjective not preceded by an article: **Dark** bread is good for you.

A. Are the adjectives in these sentences preceded or unpreceded? Check the appropriate column.

	Preceded	Unpreceded
1. I prefer to buy organic foods.	_____	✓
2. But they are only sold in expensive stores.	_____	_____
3. We like the purple grapes better.	_____	_____
4. This restaurant serves a wonderful quiche.	_____	_____
5. The homemade sausage is also served daily.	_____	_____
6. Did you all try a bite of French cheese?	_____	_____
7. Local restaurants are often cheaper.	_____	_____

KAPITEL 11

In German Adjectives can also be preceded by an article or not. However, **unpreceded adjectives** must show gender in German. Read the German sentences below. What do you observe?

adjective preceded by a **der-** word: *Dies***es** schwarze Brot schmeckt prima.
adjective preceded by an indefinite article: *Ein* schwarz**es** Brot passt gut zu diesem Käse.
adjective not preceded by an adjective: *Schwarz***es** Brot ist gut für dich.

In other words: **An unpreceded adjective must show gender, case, and number.**

Dies**er** Kaffee ist gut. Ich trinke dies**en** Kaffee nicht.	Kalt**er** Kaffee ist gut. Ich trinke kalt**en** Kaffee nicht.
Dies**e** Milch schmeckt gut. Ich trinke dies**e** Milch nicht.	Kalt**e** Milch schmeckt gut. Ich trinke kalt**e** Milch nicht.
Dies**es** Gemüse ist gesund. Ich esse dies**es** Gemüse gern.	Frisch**es** Gemüse ist gesund. Ich esse frisch**es** Gemüse gern.
Dies**e** Äpfel sind nicht gut. Ich esse dies**e** Äpfel nicht.	Grün**e** Äpfel sind nicht gut. Ich esse grün**e** Äpfel nicht.

B. Are these adjectives preceded or unpreceded by an article? Check the appropriate column.

	PRECEDED	UNPRECEDED
1. Ich habe gestern marinierten Lachs gegessen.	____	✓
2. Ich habe den marinierten Lachs schon mal gegessen.	____	____
3. Der kalte Braten schmeckt ausgezeichnet.	____	____
4. Kalter Braten schmeckt ausgezeichnet.	____	____
5. Ich mag aber diesen rohen Schinken nicht.	____	____
6. Du weißt, ich mag rohen Schinken nicht.	____	____
7. Dieser griechische Salat ist übrigens ausgezeichnet.	____	____
8. Diese gebratenen Pilze schmecken gut.	____	____
9. Isst du gern gebratene Pilze?	____	____

C. Fill in each blank with the correct form of the adjective given in parentheses.

1. (rot) Diese ____**rote**____ Grütze schmeckt phantastisch!
2. (rot) ________________ Grütze ist eine norddeutsche Spezialität.
3. (griechisch) Das ist ein ________________ Käse.
4. (griechisch) ________________ Käse ist für mich eine Delikatesse.
5. (polnisch) Diese ________________ Wurst ist ziemlich scharf.
6. (polnisch) ________________ Wurst kann ziemlich scharf sein.
7. (italienisch) Dieses ________________ Eis ist einfach lecker!
8. (italienisch) ________________ Eis ist einfach lecker.
9. (deutsch) Dieser ________________ Wein schmeckt gut zum Essen.
10. (deutsch) ________________ Wein schmeckt gut zum Essen.
11. (kalt) Ich hätte gern ________________ Wasser.
12. (warm) Das kleine Mädchen trinkt ________________ Milch nicht gern.

D. Summarize what you have learned about unpreceded adjectives in German.

____

____

____

POLITE REQUESTS (HÄTTE-FORMS)

Pupil's Edition, p. 314

In German The **hätte**-forms are also used in German **to make polite requests**. They are used to ask for something you would like to have. **Gern** is usually used with **hätte** to make a polite request.

POLITE REQUESTS
Hättest du gern mal ein Schnitzel?
Ich **hätte** gern den marinierten Lachs.

The **hätte**-forms are:

SINGULAR		PLURAL	
ich	**hätte**	wir	**hätten**
du	**hättest**	ihr	**hättet**
er, sie, es	**hätte**	sie, Sie	**hätten**

A. Make polite requests by writing a **hätte**-form in the blank provided.

1. Was **hättest** du gern zum Mittagessen?
2. Ich ____________________ gern mal ein schönes Steak.
3. Und was ____________________ ihr beiden gern zum Abendessen?
4. Wir ____________________ gern einen Gemüsesalat, und Erdbeeren als Nachtisch.
5. Weißt du, was die Antje gern ____________________ ?
6. Ich glaube, sie ____________________ gern mal marinierten Lachs.
7. Ich glaube, das ____________________ der Herr Möller auch mal gern.
8. Frag ihn mal, was er gern ____________________ !
9. Herr Möller, was ____________________ Sie denn gern zum Abendessen?

B. Write polite requests using **hätte**-forms.

1. What would you like? **Was hätten Sie gern?**
2. I'd like to have fried potatoes. ____________________
3. My mother would like a green salad. ____________________
4. Mark would like a coffee. ____________________
5. Sara and John, what would you like? ____________________
6. We'd like a glass of water. ____________________
7. Who would like to have milk? ____________________
8. We'd rather have orange juice. ____________________
9. The children would like ice cream. ____________________

C. Complete the following sentences, using a **hätte-**form and the words given in parentheses.

1. (frisch / Brot) Ich **hätte gern frisches Brot.**
2. (frisch / Erdbeeren) Wir ______________________________
3. (kalt / Saft) Hannah ______________________________
4. (heiß / Kaffee) Oma ______________________________
5. (süß / Schokolade) Die Kinder ______________________________
6. (ungarisch/ Wein) Meine Eltern ______________________________
7. (deutsch / Bier) Mein Opa ______________________________
8. (italienisch / Obst) Du ______________________________, nicht?
9. (griechisch / Käse) Ich ______________________________

D. Summarize what you have learned about making polite requests in German.

____

____

____

KAPITEL 11

Grammar Tutor Activities
Komm mit!
German 3

KAPITEL 1 (WIEDERHOLUNG)

THE CONVERSATIONAL PAST (REVIEW)

Pupil's Edition, p. 10

In German When referring to **past time** in conversation, German most often uses the **present perfect tense**, often referred to as the **conversational past**.

a. In the **present perfect tense**, you use the present tense form of either **haben** or **sein** and the **past participle** of the main verb.

Ich **habe** gestern Abend Tennis **gespielt**.
Wir **sind** mit dem Rad nach Hause **gefahren**.

b. Most **past participles** have the prefix **ge-**. **Past participles** of **weak verbs** end in **-t**, the **past participles** of **strong verbs** end in **-en** (some in **-n**), and often they have a vowel change. Since you cannot predict what the change will be, you must memorize the past participles of strong verbs.

For most weak verbs: Use the third-person singular form with the prefix **ge-**. Verbs ending in **-ieren** do not use the prefix **ge-**; the past participle is identical to the third-person singular, present tense.

(er) spielt	**ge**spielt	(sie) tanzt	**ge**tanzt
(er) telefoniert	telefoniert	(sie) fotografiert	fotografiert

For most strong verbs: Use the infinitive with the prefix **ge-**.

laufen	**ge**laufen	fahren	**ge**fahren

c. There are a few weak verbs that have vowel changes or other changes in the past participle.

(er) bringt	ge**bracht**	(sie) kennt	ge**kannt**

d. There are many strong verbs with vowel changes.

helfen	ge**holfen**	gießen	ge**gossen**

e. Separable-prefix verbs place the ge-marker between the prefix and the past participle.

einstecken	ein**ge**steckt	anziehen	an**ge**zogen

A. After having reviewed the past participles in your textbook, write the past participle for each infinitive.

1. kaufen **gekauft**
2. lesen ____________
3. anprobieren ____________
4. besuchen ____________
5. waschen ____________
6. einladen ____________
7. brauchen ____________
8. finden ____________
9. abheben ____________
10. gießen ____________
11. einkaufen ____________
12. vorschlagen ____________

13. aufräumen ________________ 14. haben ________________

15. sein ________________ 16. fernsehen ________________

B. Fill in each blank with the appropriate verb form.

1. Wann **hast** du diese Werbung (lesen) **gelesen** ?
2. Ich __________ gestern mit einer Freundin in die Stadt (gehen) __________ .
3. Wir __________ in einem Café ein Schokoladeneis (essen) __________ .
4. Ein junger Kellner aus Irland __________ uns (bedienen) __________ .
5. Ich __________ mir ein paar neue Klamotten (kaufen) __________ .
6. Du __________ dich heute aber so fein (anziehen) __________ !
7. Was, du __________ dein Handy nicht (mitnehmen) __________ ?
8. Einfach! Ich __________ es zu Hause (vergessen) __________ .
9. Wann __________ ihr denn nach Hause (kommen) __________ ?
10. Und wie lange __________ du in der Stadt (bleiben) __________ ?

C. Rewrite the following questions in the present perfect tense.

1. Wen besuchst du? **Wen hast du besucht?**
2. Was hört ihr? ________________
3. Wo schläfst du? ________________
4. Wann gehen die Kinder? ________________
5. Wie lange bleibt ihr? ________________
6. Was fotografiert er? ________________
7. Was gefällt dir nicht? ________________
8. Wen lädst du ein? ________________
9. Wo arbeitet er? ________________
10. Wie viel kostet das? ________________
11. Worüber freust du dich? ________________
12. Was schreibst du ihm? ________________

D. Summarize what you have learned in this review of the conversational past.

____

____

____

KAPITEL 2 (WIEDERHOLUNG)

ADJECTIVES (REVIEW)

Pupil's Edition, p. 48

In German Adjectives are traditionally presented in three categories: adjectives preceded by **der** and **dieser-**words, adjectives preceded by **ein-**words, and unpreceded adjectives (adjectives preceded by neither **der-** nor **ein-**words). Study the chart below.

		Masculine	Feminine	Neuter	Plural
preceded by **der-**words	Nominative	**e**	**e**	**e**	**en**
	Accusative	**en**	**e**	**e**	**en**
ein-words	Nominative	**er**	**e**	**es**	**en**
	Accusative	**en**	**e**	**es**	**en**
unpreceded	Nominative	**er**	**e**	**es**	**e**
	Accusative	**en**	**e**	**es**	**e**

a. Adjectives following **der** and **dieser-**words have the ending **-e** in all three genders and in the nominative and accusative cases, with the exception of the masculine accusative form, which is **-en**. All plural forms end in **-en**.

Der blau**e** Pulli gefällt mir. Ich kaufe mir den blau**en** Pulli.

b. Adjectives following **ein-**words, as well as unpreceded adjectives, must show gender with masculine and neuter nouns.

Dein griechisch**er** Käse schmeckt toll!
Griechisch**er** Käse schmeckt toll.

c. In the plural, adjectives following **der** and **ein-**words have the ending **-en**, unpreceded adjectives have the ending **-e**. Adjectives following numbers larger than one and words such as **einige, mehrere, viele** also end in **-e**.

Wo sind die / meine braun**en** Schuhe?
Ich trage braun**e** Schuhe gern.
Wir haben zwei groß**e** Autos in der Garage.
Und wir haben auch mehrere schön**e** Fahrräder.

d. All adjective endings in the dative (and genitive) case have the ending **-en**.

Du siehst gut aus in dem / diesem / deinem rot**en** Kleid.

KAPITEL 2

A. Fill in each blank with the correct adjective ending.

1. Wir haben unsere schön__en__ Ferien in einem klein__en__ Dorf in Hessen verbracht.
2. Wir hatten eine nett______ Wohnung mit einer sonnig______ Terrasse.
3. Im Zimmer waren zwei groß______ Betten und ein klein______ Sofa.
4. Im Haus waren auch eine schön______ Sauna und ein groß______ Fernsehraum.
5. Hinter dem schön______ Haus war ein groß______ Tennisplatz.

6. Wir sind auf die grün______ Berge gestiegen und in dem kalt______ See geschwommen.

7. In dem klein______ Dorf hat es auch einen toll______ Pool gegeben.

8. Ich habe viele schön______ Karten an mehrere alt______ Freunde geschrieben.

B. Fill in each blank with the correct adjective ending.

1. Ich habe mir eine grün__e__ Bluse und einen bunt__en__ Rock gekauft.
2. Ich habe mir eine grau______ Hose und einen schwarz______ Gürtel gekauft.
3. Wann hast du dir diesen rot______ Anorak und das fesch______ Käppi gekauft?
4. Ich habe mir einen teuer______ Tennisschläger und weiß______ Tennisschuhe gekauft.
5. Die braun______ Schuhe und das gelb______ Hemd bringe ich wieder zurück.
6. Hast du dieses toll______ Buch deiner deutsch______ Kusine gekauft?
7. Meinem krank______ Opa habe ich ein neu______ Handy gekauft.
8. Mein krank______ Opa telefoniert gern mit meiner lieb______ Oma.

C. Fill in each blank with the correct adjective ending.

1. Ich brauche ein halb__es__ Pfund Butter und mehrere frisch__e__ Eier.
2. Wir haben italienisch______ Tomaten, und die neu______ Kartoffeln sind aus Bayern.
3. Hol mir doch einen grün______ Salat und ein halb______ Kilo grün______ Bohnen.
4. Ich möchte zwei frisch______ Weißwürste und einen ofenfrisch______ Leberkäs.
5. Wir haben viel frisch______ Obst und mehrere grün______ Gurken gekauft.
6. Wir haben auch viele frisch______ Äpfel und zwei saftig______ Orangen gekauft.
7. Ich mag den bitter______ Spinat nicht und auch nicht den sauer______ Joghurt.
8. Du musst deine lecker______ Käsebrote und das saftig______ Schinkenbrot essen.

D. Fill in the blank with the correct adjective ending.

1. Der neu__e__ Film ist toll.
2. Sein neu______ Film ist toll.
3. Nur zwei neu______ Filme sind toll.
4. Viele neu______ Filme sind toll.
5. Ich sehe den neu______ Film.
6. Ich sehe seinen neu______ Film.
7. Ich sehe diese neu______ Filme.
8. Ich sehe seine neu______ Filme.

E. Summarize what you have learned in this review of adjective endings.

____

____

INFINITIVE PHRASES

Pupil's Edition, p. 75

In English An **infinitive** is an unconjugated verb usually preceded by the word *to: to help, to go, to be.* An **infinitive phrase** consists of an infinitive together with its modifiers and complements.

I am trying **to help you**.
We are ready **to go home now**.
I plan **to study German tonight**.

A. For each of the following sentences, underline the infinitive phrase. If a sentence does not contain an infinitive phrase, write *none* after the sentence.

1. We are trying to think positively.
2. I am prepared to study hard.
3. We all must work harder.
4. She's planning to fly to Europe this summer.
5. My cousins are ready to go to school in the fall.
6. Jacob plans to buy a new bicycle.
7. She should buy herself new clothes.
8. What have you decided to do after class?

Compare Look at these English sentences again and compare them to the German sentences. How is the English "to" expressed?

I am trying **to help**.	Ich versuche **zu helfen**.
I am trying **to help you**.	Ich versuche, **dir zu helfen**.
We are ready **to go home now**.	Wir sind bereit, **jetzt nach Hause zu gehen**.
I plan **to study German tonight**.	Ich habe vor, **heute Abend Deutsch zu lernen**.
I exercise a lot **in order to stay fit**.	Ich mache viel Sport, **um fit zu bleiben**.

a. In German infinitive phrases, the **infinitive** is always preceded by **zu** and is placed at the end of the sentence.

Ich versuche **zu helfen**.

b. If the infinitive is a **verb** with a **separable prefix**, such as **mitmachen**, **zu** is inserted between the prefix and the verb.

Ich habe vor mit**zu**machen.

c. When any other words are added to the infinitive, a comma precedes the infinitive clause.

Ich habe vor, heute Abend Deutsch **zu lernen**.
Ich habe keine Zeit, meine Eltern vom Flughafen **abzuholen**.

d. Infinitive clauses can be introduced by **um zu** *(in order to)* and **ohne zu** *(without ...ing)*.

Ich mache viel Sport, **um** fit **zu bleiben**. I do a lot of sports in order to stay fit.
Ich mache nie Sport, **ohne** etwas **zu essen**. I never do sports without eating something.

B. Complete the following sentences by writing infinitive phrases using the word or words in parentheses. Add commas where appropriate.

1. (lernen) Ich versuche **zu lernen.**
2. (heute Abend lernen) Ich versuche ____________________
3. (gehen) Wir haben vor ____________________
4. (ins Kino gehen) Wir haben vor ____________________
5. (abnehmen) Rainer versucht ____________________
6. (bis Ostern abnehmen) Rainer versucht ____________________
7. (aufpassen) Pam versucht ____________________
8. (heute aufpassen) Pam versucht ____________________

C. Complete each sentence using the **um . . . zu** construction and the verb or verb phrase given in parentheses.

1. (Geld sparen) Ich bleibe zu Hause, **um Geld zu sparen.**
2. (eine Reise machen) Ich spare Geld, ____________________
3. (nicht zunehmen) Ich esse vernünftig, ____________________
4. (s. ablenken) Ich mache Sport, ____________________
5. (etwas abnehmen) Ich mache Diät, ____________________
6. (s. waschen) Ich gehe nach Hause, ____________________
7. (s. die Haare waschen) Ich gehe nach Hause, ____________________
8. (s. modisch anziehen) Ich gebe viel Geld aus, ____________________

D. Write the following sentences in German.

1. I'm trying to sleep. **Ich versuche zu schlafen.**
2. I'm trying to sleep eight hours. ____________________
3. I'm planning to study. ____________________
4. I'm planning to study German tonight. ____________________
5. I do sports in order to stay fit. ____________________

E. Summarize what you have learned about German infinitive phrases.

____

KAPITEL 4

ORDINAL NUMBERS

Pupil's Edition, p. 98

KAPITEL 4

In English An **ordinal number** is a number indicating position in a series or order. The ordinal numbers are *first, second, third, fourth,* and so on. They are different from **cardinal numbers**, which indicate quantity, not order. Cardinal numbers are *one, two, three,* etc.

I have three brothers. I am the **second** oldest of us three.
January has thirty-one days. My birthday is on the **thirty-first** of January.

Ordinal numbers are also used as adjectives.

I am saving for my **first** car. I am in the **twelfth** grade.

A. Circle the ordinal numbers in the following sentences.

1. I'm arriving on the (fifteenth) of June.
2. Our vacation begins on the third of April.
3. My birthday is on the seventh of January.
4. I am the second child of four.
5. Today is my parents' twentieth anniversary.
6. The twenty-second falls on a Monday.
7. She is making her third attempt to climb this wall.

In German Almost all **ordinal numbers** add the ending **-t** or **-st** to the cardinal number. As in English, the ordinal numbers for **eins** and **drei** are slightly different from the cardinal numbers.

a. Here are some stem forms of ordinal numbers.

eins	**erst-**	zwei	zwei**t-**	drei	**dritt-**
vier	vier**t-**	fünf	fünf**t-**	sechs	sechs**t-**

Note: sieben sieb**t-** acht- ach**t-**

b. Beginning with **zwanzig**, ordinal numbers add the ending **-st** to the cardinal number.

zwanzig zwanzig**st-** einunddreißig einunddreißig**st-**

c. Since ordinal numbers are used as adjectives following **ein-**words or **der** and **dieser-**words, they have endings like any other adjective.

Hier ist mein neu**es** Auto. Hast du den neu**en** Film auch gesehen?
Hier ist mein erst**es** Auto. Hast du den zweit**en** Film auch gesehen?

d. In writing, German uses a period after a numeral to make it an ordinal number. However, you still must be able to articulate what the abbreviation stands for.

der **1.** Mai = der **erste** Mai am **13.** März = am **dreizehnten** März

KAPITEL 4

B. Write in each blank the correct form of the ordinal number given. Note that in this activity, all ordinal numbers follow the definite article.

1. Wer hat am (7.) **siebten** Mai Geburtstag?
2. Der (3.) ______________ Januar ist ein Montag.
3. Heute ist der (31.) ______________ Oktober.
4. Wir haben am (8.) ______________ Juni Ferien.
5. Unsere Ferien beginnen erst am (14.) ______________ Juli.
6. In der (1.) ______________ Stunde haben wir Bio.
7. Mathe haben wir erst in der (2.) ______________ Stunde.
8. Milwaukee, den (18.) ______________ Dezember, 2002
9. Ich habe heute schon den (2.) ______________ Film gesehen.

C. Write in each blank the correct form of the ordinal number given. Note that in this activity, all ordinal numbers follow **ein-**words.

1. Wie hast du denn deinen (15.) **fünfzehnten** Geburtstag verbracht?
2. An meinem (16.) ______________ Geburtstag fahre ich nach Chicago.
3. Ich habe gestern meinen (1.) ______________ Ferientag gehabt.
4. Wir haben schon unser (3.) ______________ Auto kaputt gemacht.
5. Wenn ich 18 bin, will ich mir meinen (1.) ______________ Wagen kaufen.
6. Ich habe schon meinen (4.) ______________ Brief zurückbekommen.
7. Meine Mutter hat gestern ihren (40.) ______________ Geburtstag gehabt.
8. Du hast jetzt schon dein (2.) ______________ Pausenbrot gegessen.
9. Meine Großeltern haben morgen ihren (50.) ______________ Hochzeitstag.

D. Summarize what you have learned about German ordinal numbers.

____

____

RELATIVE PRONOUNS AND RELATIVE CLAUSES *Pupil's Edition, p. 99*

In English A **relative pronoun** is a word that refers to a previously mentioned noun or pronoun, called its *antecedent.* A relative pronoun introduces a **relative clause**, which describes the antecedent. It also has its own subject and verb separate from the subject and verb of the main clause. English has three relative pronouns: who (whom, whose), which, and that.

The boy **who** plays tennis is in my class.	(who refers to a person, the boy)
I have Math, **which** I like.	(which refers to a thing, Math)
A type of music **that** I don't like is country.	(that refers to a thing, music)

The relative pronoun can function as the the subject of the clause, the direct or indirect object of the clause, or the object of a preposition.

a. It can be the the subject:

The boy who plays tennis is in my class.	(who is the subject of *plays*)
I had to get a shot, which hurt.	(which is the subject of *hurt*)

b. It can be the object:

This is the girl whom I saw at the game.	(whom is the direct object of *saw*)
The girl whom I sent a letter never answered.	(whom is the indirect object of *sent*)

c. It can be the object of a preposition:

This is the student with whom I am not speaking. (whom is the object of *with*)

d. In English, the relative pronouns are often understood and therefore are omitted.

This is the girl (whom) I met at the game.
This is a subject (that) I had last year.

A. In each of the following sentences, underline the relative clause and circle the antecedent of the relative pronoun.

1. Where does the friend who called you last night live?
2. Here is a book that I enjoyed reading.
3. Cookies that have raisins in them are my favorite.
4. Here comes the girl with whom I'm not speaking.
5. Over there is the math teacher I had last year.
6. He is buying the same computer that he used at his friend's house.

B. Rewrite each pair of sentences as one sentence with a main clause and a relative clause.

1. Mom went to the supermarket. It is nearby.

Mom went to the supermarket that is nearby.

2. The girls are coming along. They sing in the choir.

____

3. My friend Jacob will be here soon. I went to the movies with him last weekend.

____

4. I like clothes. They are comfortable and inexpensive.

____

5. The guy is in the hospital. He was injured on the trail.

____

6. We're talking about the math teacher. He gives really hard tests.

____

7. The team is even better this year. They went to the championship last year.

____

8. There is the raccoon. It always knocks over our trash cans.

____

In German When using a **relative pronoun** to introduce a **relative clause**, the choice of relative pronoun depends on:

a. the **gender** and **number** of the antecedent

Hier ist **der Junge, der** gut Tennis spielt. (Junge: masculine)
Hier sind **die Schüler, die** gut Schach spielen. (die Schüler: plural)

b. the **case** of the **relative pronoun**, which is determined by its function in the relative clause as a subject, direct object, indirect object, or object of a preposition.

Hier ist der Junge, **der** gut Tennis spielt.
(der [Junge] spielt gut Tennis: subject)
Hier ist der Junge, **den** ich am Strand getroffen habe.
(Ich habe den [Jungen] getroffen: direct object)
Hier ist der Junge, **dem** ich eine E-Mail geschickt habe.
(Ich habe dem [Jungen] eine E-Mail geschickt: indirect object)
Die Uhr, **für die** ich mich interessiere, kostet 85 Euro.
Ich interessiere mich für die [Uhr]: object of a preposition)

c. In German relative pronouns are never omitted.

This is a subject I like. Das ist ein Fach, **das** ich gern habe.
This is a film I saw before. Das ist ein Film, **den** ich schon gesehen habe.

d. A relative clause is a dependent clause, and the conjugated verb must always be in last position in the clause. Notice that the relative clause is always set apart by one or two commas, depending on if the relative clause ends the sentence or is in the middle.

Hier ist der Junge, **den** ich am Strand getroffen **habe**.
Die Uhr, für **die** ich mich **interessiere**, kostet 85 Euro.

Here are the forms of the relative pronouns:

	MASCULINE	FEMININE	NEUTER	PLURAL
Nominative	**der**	**die**	**das**	**die**
Accusative	**den**	**die**	**das**	**die**
Dative	**dem**	**der**	**dem**	**denen**
Genitive	**dessen**	**deren**	**dessen**	**deren**

C. Underline the relative clause in each sentence, then circle both the relative pronoun and its antecedent.

1. Ich habe Eltern, die ganz vernünftig und tolerant sind.
2. Mein Bruder, der drei Jahre älter ist, geht in die gleiche Schule.
3. Ich habe viele Freunde, mit denen ich mich gut verstehe.
4. Ich habe auch einen Freund, mit dem ich am Samstag ins Kino gehe.
5. Eine Lehrerin, mit der ich mich gut verstehe, trifft sich mit uns nach der Schule.
6. Ich bin auch in einer Clique, die sich immer am Freitag trifft.
7. Meine Freundin, mit der ich in den Ferien weg war, ist auch in der Clique.
8. Oft gehen wir in ein Café, das gleich in der Nähe ist.
9. Dort sprechen wir über ein Problem, das wir alle haben: viel Zeit und wenig Geld.

D. Rewrite each pair of sentences as one sentence with a main clause and a relative clause. Note that the relative clause immediately follows the noun to which it refers.

1. Die Clique ist ziemlich groß. Der gehöre ich an.

   Die Clique, der ich angehöre, ist ziemlich groß.

2. Mein Opa kommt zu meiner Party. Der ist schon siebzig Jahre alt.

   ____

3. Die Mädchen kommen auch. Die singen im Chor mit.

   ____

4. Die Leute sind älter als ich. Mit denen gehe ich ab und zu aus.

   ____

5. Der Mathelehrer ist erst 30 Jahre alt. Über den reden wir gern.

   ____

6. Diese Schüler sind in meiner Klasse. Die kommen in diesem Café zusammen.

   ____

7. Dort kommt meine Freundin. Mit der gehe ich heute Abend ins Kino.

   ____

8. Mein Opa wohnt am Bodensee. Ich fliege mit ihm nach Milwaukee.

____

9. Meine Kusine kommt uns besuchen. Ich war mit ihr an der Nordsee.

____

KAPITEL 4

E. Fill in the blanks with the correct relative pronoun.

1. Die Freunde, ___die___ ich jetzt anrufe, fahren mit an die Nordsee.
2. Die Freunde, mit __________ ich an die Nordsee fahre, haben tolle Räder.
3. Wann fährst du zu deinem Cousin, __________ am Bodensee wohnt?
4. Mein Opa, __________ du letztes Jahr kennen gelernt hast, kommt uns besuchen.
5. Das ist mein Opa, __________ ich immer am Wochenende im Garten helfe.
6. Im Garten arbeiten ist ein Job, für __________ ich mich interessiere.
7. Meine Freundin, mit __________ ich gern jogge, hat sich den Fuss verstaucht.
8. Kennst du die Samantha, __________ oft mit mir joggt?
9. Wir haben morgen eine Matheprüfung, für __________ ich noch lernen muss.
10. Aber die Deutscharbeit, __________ wir morgen haben, soll einfach sein.

F. Write the following sentences in German.

1. The movie I saw last night was great.

   Der Film, den ich gestern Abend gesehen habe, war toll.

2. The friend I visited lives in Berlin.

   ____

3. The song I just heard is very popular.

   ____

4. The letter you wrote is too long.

   ____

5. The e-mail I got is from my mom.

   ____

6. I like the photos you took.

   ____

G. Summarize what you have learned about German relative clauses.

____

____

CONDITIONAL SENTENCES

Pupil's Edition, p. 104

In English You have been using the *would*-forms in sentences expressing wishes.

I **would** go to Eisenach. He **would** eat a sandwich.

You also use *would* and the dictionary form of the verb (without *to*) in a construction called the **conditional**. The conditional is used:

a. **when hypothesizing** in so-called "if . . . then" constructions

If I **had** money, I **would** go to Australia. (But you don't have the money.)
If you **were** rich, you **would** buy a new car. (But you are not rich.)

b. **in polite requests**

Would you please call me this afternoon?

A. Fill in each blank with an appropriate verb form.

1. If I **were** richer, I **would** buy you a new soccer ball.
2. If I ______________ the time, I ______________ jog with you tonight.
3. If we ______________ the patience, we ______________ wait until tomorrow.
4. If she ______________ sick, she ______________ stay at home in bed.
5. If Derrick ______________ won the match, he ______________ be in Paris now.
6. If the children ______________ naughty, they ______________ not get their presents.

In German You have used the **würde-**forms and the **hätte-**forms in sentences expressing polite requests.

Würdest du mit mir in ein griechisches Lokal gehen?
Ich **hätte** gern mal den marinierten Lachs.

A **würde-**form together with a form of **hätte** or **wäre** is used in **conditional clauses** when making hypotheses.

a. The **wenn-**clause is used to introduce the clause, followed by the **würde-**form.

Wenn wir Zeit **hätten, würden** wir ins Kino **gehen**.
Wenn ich krank **wäre, würde** ich zu Hause **bleiben**.

b. You may begin with the **würde-**clause and follow with the **wenn-**clause. In questions, you always start with the **würde-**clause.

Wir **würden** ins Kino **gehen**, wenn wir Zeit **hätten**.
Was **würdet** ihr tun, wenn ihr Zeit **hättet**?

c. Here are the verb forms:

ich, er, sie, es	**hätte**	**wäre**	**würde**
du	**hättest**	**wärest**	**würdest**
wir, sie, Sie	**hätten**	**wären**	**würden**
ihr	**hättet**	**wäret**	**würdet**

KAPITEL 4

B. Fill in each blank with the correct verb form.

1. Was **würdest** du tun, wenn du vier Wochen Ferien **hättest** ?
2. Wenn ich vier Wochen Ferien ________________ , ________________ ich Tennis spielen.
3. Was ________________ ihr alles kaufen, wenn ihr viel Geld ________________ ?
4. Wenn wir viel Geld ________________ , ________________ wir eine Reise machen.
5. Was ____________ Mary essen, wenn sie großen Hunger ________________ ?
6. Wenn Mary großen Hunger ________________ , ________________ sie ein Steak essen.
7. Wohin ________________ deine Eltern fliegen, wenn sie Ferien ________________ ?
8. Wenn meine Eltern Ferien ________________ , ________________ sie nach Bali fliegen.
9. Was ____________ ihr trinken, wenn ihr Durst ________________ ?
10. Wenn wir Durst ________________ , ________________ wir viel Wasser trinken.

C. Write conditional sentences, beginning each one with the **wenn**-clause.

1. ich Zeit haben / mit dir an den Strand gehen

   Wenn ich Zeit hätte, würde ich mit dir an den Strand gehen.

2. Max Hunger haben / eine große Pizza essen

   ____

3. wir Durst haben / Wasser mit viel Eis trinken

   ____

4. du Glück haben / das Schachspiel gewinnen

   ____

5. wir in München sein / zum Oktoberfest gehen

   ____

6. ich in Berlin sein / eine Bootsfahrt auf der Havel machen

   ____

7. ihr in Hamburg sein / in einem feinen Hotel übernachten

   ____

D. Summarize what you have learned about conditional sentences.

____

____

THE POSSESSIVE: GENITIVE CASE

Pupil's Edition, p. 105

In English The word **possessive** refers to the ownership of one noun by another.

In English you can show possession in two different ways:

a. You can use an **apostrophe**:

The Supreme Court's judgment is final. I don't like the car's color.

b. You can use the word **of** and an article:

The judgment **of the** Supreme Court is final. I don't like the color **of the** car.

KAPITEL 4

A. Circle the elements that indicate possession.

1. Do you know the color (of) the book?
2. Have you seen Jordan's math test?
3. The scent of a rose is wonderful.
4. Jack's house is on a river.
5. What is the name of the state flower of Texas?
6. She is dating the son of the mayor.

In German There are various ways of showing **possession** in German.

a. Use the ending **-s** with **proper names**. No apostrophe is used in German!

Das ist Peter**s** Auto. That is Peter's car.

b. You can also use the **genitive case** to indicate possession. To do this, you use the genitive case form of **der**, **dieser**-words, and **ein**-words, and add **-es** to most **masculine** and **neuter nouns** of one syllable, and **-s** to **masculine** and **neuter nouns** of more than one syllable.

one syllable:	das Auto de**s** Freund**es** der Besuch ein**es** Freund**es**	die Farbe de**s** Buch**es** der Preis dies**es** Buch**es**
more than one syllable:	das Auto des Lehrer**s** das Auto dies**es** Lehrer**s**	die Farbe de**s** Auto**s** die Farbe mein**es** Auto**s**

Note: Masculine nouns ending in **-e** add **-n** in the genitive case.

das Auto d**es** Junge**n**

c. **Feminine** and **plural nouns** add no special genitive endings. Only the articles or adjectives show the genitive case form **-er**.

feminine nouns:	das Auto d**er** / dies**er** Lehrerin	das Auto mein**er** Mutter
plural nouns:	der Preis d**er** / dies**er** Bücher	der Preis dies**er** Autos

d. In colloquial German you may also use the preposition **von** and the dative case to show possession.

GENITIVE	DATIVE
Das ist das Auto mein**er** Mutter.	Das ist das Auto von mein**er** Mutter.
Das ist das Auto mein**es** Vater**s**.	Das ist das Auto von mein**em** Vater.

KAPITEL 4

B. Fill in each blank with the correct genitive form of the words in parentheses.

1. (meine Eltern) Hier ist das Haus **meiner Eltern** .
2. (der Opa) Das ist das Lieblingsauto ________________ .
3. (ein Freund) Herta ist die Kusine ________________ .
4. (meine Freundin) Kennst du den Vater ________________ ?
5. (deine Freunde) Die Geschichten ________________ sind toll!
6. (diese Stadt) Das Rathaus ________________ ist sehr alt.
7. (unsere Hauptstadt) Hier ist das Wappen ________________ .
8. (das Land Bayern) Kennst du die Farben ________________ ?
9. (ihre Tochter) Wo lebt der Vater ________________ ?

C. Complete each of the following answers using genitive case forms.

1. Gehört das Boot deinem Vater? Ja, das ist das Boot **meines Vaters** .
2. Gehört das Auto deiner Tante? Ja, das ist das Auto ________________ .
3. Gehört das Obst deinen Kindern? Ja, das ist das Obst ________________ .
4. Gehört das Rad seinem Freund? Ja, das ist das Rad ________________ .
5. Gehört der Hund dem Opa? Ja, das ist der Hund ________________ .
6. Gehört die Katze der Großmutter? Ja, das ist die Katze ________________ .
7. Gehören die CDs dem Mädchen? Ja, das sind die CDs ________________ .
8. Gehören die Häuser der Stadt? Ja, das sind die Häuser ________________ .

D. Rewrite the following sentences using genitive case forms.

1. Das ist das Auto von meinem Vater. **Das ist das Auto meines Vaters.**
2. Wo ist das Haus von deiner Tante? ________________
3. Wo ist das Hotel von deinen Eltern? ________________
4. Wo ist die E-Mail von deinem Freund? ________________
5. Ich höre das Bellen von ihrem Hund. ________________
6. Hier sind die Bücher von den Kindern. ________________
7. Wo ist das Rad von meinem Onkel? ________________

E. Summarize what you have learned about the genitive case.

____

____

KAPITEL 5

MODAL VERBS: PAST TENSE

Pupil's Edition, p. 133

In English The **past tense of modals** is formed in two ways:

a. by changing the form of the verb.

He can leave now. — He **could** have left after 10 o'clock.

b. by using a different verb.

We must go now. — We **had to** leave early.

A. Check whether the following sentences refer to present time or past time.

	PRESENT	PAST
1. I could not come to band practice.	____	✓
2. We want to practice tonight.	____	____
3. I had to be home by 9 o'clock.	____	____
4. I have to be home by 9:30.	____	____
5. We must leave in the morning.	____	____
6. We had to leave in the morning.	____	____
7. She could not imagine this!	____	____

In German The **past tense** (imperfect) **of modals** are used in the same position as present-tense modals, but they have a slightly different form.

Present tense: Wir müssen um 7 Uhr nach Hause gehen.
Past tense: Wir **mussten** um 7 Uhr nach Hause gehen.

a. In the past tense, modals do not have an umlaut, and they have a past-tense marker to indicate past tense. This marker is **-t**, used between the stem and the ending. The verb **mögen** has the the **mochte-**forms in the past tense.

	dürfen	müssen	können	mögen	sollen	wollen
ich	durf**te**	muss**te**	konn**te**	moch**te**	soll**te**	woll**te**
du	durf**test**	muss**test**	konn**test**	moch**test**	soll**test**	woll**test**
er	durf**te**	muss**te**	konn**te**	moch**te**	soll**te**	woll**te**
wir	durf**ten**	muss**ten**	konn**ten**	moch**ten**	soll**ten**	woll**ten**
ihr	durf**tet**	muss**tet**	konn**tet**	moch**tet**	soll**tet**	woll**tet**
sie	durf**ten**	muss**ten**	konn**ten**	moch**ten**	soll**ten**	woll**ten**

b. Modals do have a perfect tense to indicate past time. However, the imperfect tense is preferred when referring to past time because it is shorter and easier to use.

Perfect tense: Wir **haben** schon um 9 Uhr nach Hause gehen **müssen**.
Imperfect: Wir **mussten** schon um 9 Uhr nach Hause **gehen**.

B. Complete each sentence by filling in the blank with the correct imperfect form of the modal given in parentheses.

1. (können) Warum **konntest** du nicht mit mir ins Kino gehen?
2. (müssen) Ich ______________________ gestern Abend Hausaufgaben machen.
3. (wollen) Warum ______________________ ihr gestern Abend nicht fernsehen?
4. (können) Die Marietta ______________________ gestern nicht in die Schule gehen.
5. (mögen) Warum ______________________ du nicht den Nachtisch essen?
6. (sollen) Wir ______________________ gestern noch für die Oma einkaufen gehen.
7. (dürfen) Die Hannah ______________________ nicht ihre eigene Meinung sagen.
8. (können) Wer ______________________ denn mit den Ausländern sprechen?
9. (müssen) Die Schüler ______________________ nach der Schule im Schulchor singen.

C. Write the following sentences in German.

1. I couldn't go to school today. **Ich konnte heute nicht zur Schule gehen.**
2. I had to help at home. ______________________
3. He could not call me. ______________________
4. She wanted to send an e-mail. ______________________
5. We did not want to stay. ______________________
6. I was supposed to tell you that. ______________________
7. Did you have to stay home alone? ______________________

D. Summarize what you have learned about the past tense of modal verbs.

____

____

KAPITEL 6

NARRATIVE PAST (IMPERFECT)

Pupil's Edition, p. 155

In English The **past tense** is used to express something that happened in the past. There are several verb forms that show that the action happened in the past.

I played	simple past (so called because only one word is used)
I was playing	past progressive
I did play	emphatic past

The other compound tenses for expressing the past are the perfect tenses.

A. Underline the simple past forms in the following sentences.

1. Who watched the movie last night?
2. We played soccer.
3. Who said we came back in the evening?
4. Who heard the news this morning?
5. They saw us as soon as we left the house.
6. I bought you an ice cream cone.

In German German does not have a past progressive tense or an emphatic past tense. German has two main tenses to express action in the past:

a. the **present perfect**, or **conversational past**, with two verb forms:

Ich **habe** gestern Tennis **gespielt**.

b. the **narrative past** or the **imperfect**, often referred to as **simple past**, with only one verb form:

Ich **spielte** den ganzen Abend Tennis.

Forms of the narrative past tense:

Weak verbs add the past-tense marker **-te** to the verb stem. First and second person have no further endings.

Strong verbs often have a vowel change in the imperfect: geben – g**a**b, sehen – s**a**h. First- and third-person singular add no ending to the verb stem.

Present Tense		Weak Verbs Past Tense		Strong Verbs Past Tense	
ich	spiele	ich	spiel**te**	ich	g**a**b
du	spielst	du	spiel**te**st	du	g**a**b**st**
er, sie, es, man	spielt	er, sie, es, man	spiel**te**	er, sie, es, man	g**a**b
wir	spielen	wir	spiel**te**n	wir	g**a**b**en**
ihr	spielt	ihr	spiel**te**t	ihr	g**a**b**t**
sie, Sie	spielen	sie, Sie	spiel**te**n	sie, Sie	g**a**b**en**

c. Here is a small sample of strong verbs with their vowel changes in the imperfect.

kommen - kam	fahren - fuhr	verlieren - verlor	schlafen - schlief
essen - aß	tragen - trug	anziehen - zog an	gefallen - gefiel

d. There are some other verbs that have a **-te** past tense marker, as well as a vowel change in the imperfect.

INFINITIVE	kennen	nennen	denken	bringen	wissen
IMPERFECT	**kannte**	**nannte**	**dachte**	**brachte**	**wusste**

e. The **narrative past**, as the name implies, **is used in narration** when someone narrates longer sequences of events, especially in writing. In narration, we generally use the first and third persons of the verb, but hardly ever the second person.

B. Having reviewed imperfect forms of verbs, both weak and strong, fill in each blank with the correct imperfect form of the verb given in the present tense.

1. ich fahre ich **fuhr**
2. ich sehe ich ____________
3. ich kenne ich ____________
4. ich trinke ich ____________
5. er spricht er ____________
6. er denkt er ____________
7. ich frage ich ____________
8. ich höre ich ____________
9. ich komme ich ____________
10. ich esse ich ____________
11. er schläft er ____________
12. es gibt es ____________

C. Fill in each blank with the correct past-tense form of the verb in parentheses.

1. (verbringen) Wir **verbrachten** unsere Ferien auf der Insel Rügen.
2. (wohnen) Wir ____________ dort in einer kleinen Pension.
3. (essen) Wir ____________ gewöhnlich in einem kleinen Lokal.
4. (fahren) Meine Eltern ____________ oft ins Dorf.
5. (kaufen) Dort ____________ sie Geschenke für die Großeltern.
6. (gefallen) Uns ____________ diese große Insel sehr.
7. (finden) Wir ____________ die Strände und das Wasser sauber.
8. (liegen / lesen) Ich ____________ oft allein am Strand und ____________ .
9. (regnen/spielen) Wenn es ____________ , ____________ wir Karten.

D. Summarize what you have learned about the narrative past, or the imperfect.

____

____

SUPERLATIVE FORMS OF ADJECTIVES

In English When adjectives are used to compare the relative intensity of nouns they modify, they change their forms. The change is called **comparison**. There are three degrees of comparison: **positive**, **comparative**, and **superlative**.

a. The positive degree describes the quality of only one person or thing. For this you use the adjective as is.

My grandma is ***old***. My bike is ***new***.

b. The comparative degree compares the intensity of a quality of one person or thing with another person or thing. For this, ***-er*** is added to the positive form of short adjectives, and ***more*** is used before long adjectives.

My father is old***er*** than his brother. My bike is new***er*** than yours.
My wife is ***more*** beautiful than ever. Our car was ***more*** expensive than his.

c. The superlative degree expresses the highest degree of intensity. For this, ***-est*** is added to short adjectives, and ***most*** is used before long adjectives.

Holly is the young***est*** student in class. Mark is the ***most*** intelligent student.

A. Read these sentences and determine whether the adjective used in each one is in the positive, comparative, or superlative degree. Check the correct column.

	Positive	Comparative	Superlative
1. My suit was more expensive than that.	____	✓	____
2. He bought the most expensive boots.	____	____	____
3. I also buy expensive things.	____	____	____
4. She likes to read a good book.	____	____	____
5. I've read better books than this.	____	____	____
6. This is the best book I've ever read.	____	____	____
7. We had the hottest weather in July.	____	____	____
8. It was hotter than in August.	____	____	____

In German The same degrees of **comparison** exist in German. The **superlative** is similar to English as far as endings go, for example: old – old**est**; alt – ält**est**.

a. As in the case of comparative forms, most adjectives of one syllable take an umlaut in the superlative form and the ending **-st**. Adjectives that end in **-d**, **-t**, **-sch**, **-ß**, **-z** add **-est**.

		Superlative			Superlative
arm	ärmer	ärm**st-**	klein	kleiner	klein**st-**
alt	älter	ält**est-**	kurz	kürzer	kürz**est-**

b. Several adjectives have irregular forms in both the comparative and the superlative.

gern	lieber	**liebst-**	gut	besser	**best-**
viel	mehr	**meist-**	nah	näher	**nächst-**

c. **Superlative forms** are most often used as adjectives preceding nouns, and, like any other adjective, **take regular adjective endings**.

kalt	käl**test-**	Der Januar ist bei uns der kältest**e** Monat.
schön	schön**st-**	Wir hatten dieses Jahr den schönst**en** Sommer.

d. Superlative forms are also used in phrases with **am** and the ending **-(e)sten**.

Im Juni war das Wetter **am** schön**sten**. In June the weather was **the most beautiful**.

B. Write the superlative adjective form before each noun.

1. (lang) der **längste** Tag
2. (viel) das ________ Geld
3. (jung) die ________ Tochter
4. (klein) das ________ Kind
5. (hoch) der ________ Berg
6. (alt) der ________ Mann
7. (kurz) der ________ Tag
8. (kalt) der ________ Winter
9. (gut) die ________ Jahre
10. (groß) das ________ Auto

C. Fill in each blank with the correct superlative form of the adjective in parentheses.

1. Letztes Jahr hatten wir den (kalt) **kältesten** Winter.
2. Wir kletterten auf den (hoch) ________ Berg in den Tiroler Alpen.
3. Meine (jung) ________ Schwester wird sieben Jahre alt.
4. Was soll ich bloß meiner (alt) ________ Schwester schenken?
5. Das ist die (gut) ________ Arbeit, die du je geschrieben hast.
6. Sag mal, wann haben wir denn den (lang) ________ Tag?
7. Weißt du, wer das (viel) ________ Geld verdient?
8. Das war das (hart) ________ Bett, auf dem ich je geschlafen habe.
9. Bald kommen die (warm) ________ Tage des Jahres.

D. Complete each of the following sentences using **am** and the superlative degree of the adjective in parentheses.

1. Meine Eltern sagen, am Rhein ist es (schön) **am schönsten**.
2. Aber mir gefällt es in den Bergen (gut) ________.
3. Ich glaube, in Sibiren ist es (kalt) ________.
4. Anfang Juli sind die Tage (lang) ________.
5. Die Luftverschmutzung stört mich (viel) ________.
6. Ich möchte (gern) ________ auf dem Land wohnen.

E. Summarize what you have learned about the superlative degree of adjectives.

____

KAPITEL 7

RELATIVE CLAUSES (CONTINUED)

Pupil's Edition, p. 193

In English In **relative clauses** we use different **relative pronouns** to refer back to the preceding clause.

a. When there is an indefinite antecedent, we generally do not use a relative pronoun to introduce the relative clause.

That is something (that) I really like.

b. Look at the following sentences containing relative clauses. Can you identify the antecedents?

I just saw the lady **who** used to be my teacher.
We saw a great movie **that** we will never forget.
My friends called me, **which** I found very nice of them.
We went to the city of Weimar, **where** the poet Goethe lived.

A. Fill in each blank with the correct relative pronoun.

1. Do you know the teacher ____**who**____ won a national award?
2. That is something ________________ I read in the paper this morning.
3. My aunt called me about this article, ________________ I found very sweet of her.
4. My uncle also called me about the article ________________ was in this morning's paper.
5. The article ________________ appeared in today's paper is not quite true.
6. I'm going to Bremen, ________________ my aunt and uncle live.

In German The word **was** introduces a relative clause when it refers back to:

a. indefinite pronouns such as **das**, **alles**, **etwas**, **nichts**, **wenig**, **viel**.

Das ist ***etwas***, **was** mir sehr gut gefallen hat.
Das ist wirklich ***alles***, **was** ich darüber weiß.

b. the entire idea of the preceding clause.

Mein Freunde haben mich angerufen, **was** ich wirklich ganz toll gefunden habe.

c. The word **wo** is used to refer to places, especially in a broader sense.

Wir haben Frankfurt besucht, **wo** Goethe 1749 geboren wurde.
Ich bin wieder in den Buchladen gegangen, **wo** ich diese Bücher gekauft habe.

d. Relative clauses are dependent clauses. The conjugated verb must be in last position. Note the position of the verbs in the clauses above.

B. Fill in each blank with the correct relative pronoun.

1. Ist das alles, ___**was**___ du geschrieben hast?
2. Du hast mir keine E-Mail geschickt, ____________ ich nicht sehr nett finde.
3. Ich lese nichts, ____________ ich schrecklich oder langweilig finde.
4. Wir waren in Eisenach in dem Haus, ____________ J.S. Bach geboren wurde.
5. Darf ich Sie etwas fragen, ____________ ich nicht verstehe?
6. Es gibt wenig, ____________ ich nicht schon mal gesehen habe.
7. Ich habe viel gehört, ____________ auch dich interessieren würde.
8. Ich lese eben, dass das Haus, ____________ Richard gewohnt hat, abgebrannt ist.

C. Write the following sentences in German. Remember that German always uses relative pronouns.

1. That's all I know. **Das ist alles, was ich weiß.**
2. There's a lot you don't know. ____________
3. That's something I can use. ____________
4. There's little I need. ____________
5. I write nothing I can't say. ____________
6. You wrote, which I find great! ____________
7. That's all I said. ____________
8. I repeat everything I hear. ____________

D. Summarize what you have learned about introducing relative clauses that refer to indefinite pronouns or that have indefinite antecedents.

____

____

____

KAPITEL 8

CONJUNCTIONS

Pupil's Edition, pp. 215-216

In English Words that join other words, phrases, or clauses are called **conjunctions**. Here are two types of conjunctions.

a. Words such as ***and***, ***or***, ***but*** are called **coordinating conjunctions**. They join clauses of equal rank.

I play soccer, **and** my sister plays tennis.
John likes jazz, **but** Mary likes classical music.
Do you want to go to the beach, **or** do you want to go to the park?

b. Words such as ***because***, ***when***, ***before*** are called **subordinating conjunctions**. They join a subordinate clause to the main clause, since the thought expressed in the subordinate clause does not convey the entire meaning on its own.

We had a lot to do **before** we went to the beach.
I am late for school **because** my alarm did not go off.

A. Underline the conjunctions in each of these sentences.

1. I said this to you because I was afraid I would hurt you.
2. I don't know what I said, but I know that I was right.
3. Dustin, you must wash your car before you take us to the concert.
4. You must wash the car, and then you must wax it, too.
5. I did not call you last night because I was angry at you.
6. Call me tonight, and I promise I will not hang up on you.

KAPITEL 8

In German The German **conjunctions** are also divided into **coordinating conjunctions** and **subordinating conjunctions**.

a. **Coordinating conjunctions** join two **coordinate (main) clauses**. The coordinating conjunctions are **und**, **oder**, **aber**, **denn**. When two main clauses or coordinate clauses are joined, the word order in both clauses remains the same: the verb is in **second position**.

Ich spiele Fußball. Meine Schwester spielt Tennis.
Ich spiele Fußball, **und** meine Schwester spielt Tennis.
John liebt Jazz. Mary liebt klassische Musik.
John liebt Jazz, **aber** Mary liebt klasssische Musik.

b. **Subordinating conjunctions** also join two clauses, a **main clause** and a **subordinate clause**. Some of the subordinating conjunctions are **dass** *(that)*, **als** *(when, at the time when)*, **wenn** *(when, whenever)*, **weil** *(because)*, **während** *(while, during)*, **ob** *(whether)*, **damit** *(so that)*. When a subordinating clause is joined to a main clause, the conjugated verb must be at the end of the subordinate clause, and a comma must be used to join the clauses.

Ich spiele jetzt Tennis. Meine Schwester spielt jetzt Schach.
Ich spiele jetzt Fußball, **weil** meine Schwester jetzt Schach **spielt**.
Wir kommen sofort, **wenn** du uns **anrufst**.

B. In each coordinate or subordinate clause, underline the conjunction and circle the conjugated verb.

1. Wir fliegen nach Florida, und wir mieten uns dort ein Auto.
2. Wir mieten uns ein Auto, wenn wir am Flughafen ankommen.
3. Wir haben ein Motelzimmer, damit wir uns erst einmal ausruhen können.
4. Am Strand ist es sehr schön, aber wir dürfen nur einen Tag dort bleiben.
5. Ich glaube aber, dass wir wieder einmal hierher kommen.
6. Als wir in Los Angeles waren, haben wir uns das Getty-Museum angesehen.
7. Es hat uns echt gefallen, weil das Museum viele gute Maler ausstellt.
8. Wir wollten noch einmal hinauffahren, aber wir hatten dann keine Zeit mehr.

C. Combine each pair of sentences using the conjunction in parentheses.

1. (weil) Ich fliege nach Deutschland. Ich möchte Deutsch lernen.
   Ich fliege nach Deutschland, weil ich Deutsch lernen möchte.
2. (damit) Ich wohne bei einer deutschen Familie. Ich lerne die Gebräuche kennen.
   ____
3. (und) Meine Gastfamilie hat zwei Kinder. Die sind so in meinem Alter.
   ____
4. (damit) Ich höre die Deutsche Welle. Ich weiß auch ein bisschen über Politik.
   ____
5. (damit) Ich nehme meinen Laptop mit. Ich kann meinen Freunden E-Mails schicken.
   ____
6. (weil) So ein Laptop ist prima. Ich kann dann drüben die Zeitung lesen.
   ____
7. (aber) Ich möchte dir eine E-Mail schicken. Ich habe deine Adresse nicht mehr.
   ____
8. (weil) Schick mir deine E-Mail-Adresse. Ich möchte dir E-Mails schicken.
   ____

D. Summarize what you have learned about German conjunctions.

____

____

____

KAPITEL 8

KAPITEL 9

SUBJUNCTIVE FORMS OF MODALS

Pupil's Edition, p. 242

Compare In both English and German, the **subjunctive** can be used to express:

a. **contrary-to-fact conditions**

Wenn ich Zeit **hätte**, **würde** ich mit dir ins Kino **gehen**. (but I don't have time)
Wenn ich in München **wäre**, **würde** ich aufs Oktoberfest **gehen**. (but I'm not there)

b. **polite requests**

Würdest du heute mit mir ins Kino **gehen**?

c. **a variety of attitudes** or **wishes** for something that could or should be done. Look at these sentences involving **modal verbs**, and determine the English meanings.

Ich **könnte** morgen mit dir ins Kino gehen.	I *could go* . . . (if nothing else came up)
Ich **müsste** aber um 9 Uhr zu Hause sein.	But I *would have to be* . . . (or else!)
Du **dürftest** nicht hier bleiben.	You *wouldn't be allowed* to stay here.
Man **sollte** das Auto billiger verkaufen.	One *should* sell the car cheaper.
Ich **wollte** ich **wäre** in Hamburg.	I *wish* I *were* in Hamburg. (But I'm not.)

d. The verb forms of the modals and of **sein** used to express such attitudes or wishes are based on the imperfect forms of these verbs. With the exception of **sollte** and **wollte**, they all have the umlaut and endings of the imperfect.

INFINITIVE	können	müssen	dürfen	sollen	wollen	sein
IMPERFECT	**konnte**	**musste**	**durfte**	**sollte**	**wollte**	**war**
ich	**könnte**	**müsste**	**dürfte**	**sollte**	**wollte**	**wäre**
du	**könntest**	**müsstest**	**dürftest**	**solltest**	**wolltest**	**wär(e)st**
er, sie, es	**könnte**	**müsste**	**dürfte**	**sollte**	**wollte**	**wäre**
wir	**könnten**	**müssten**	**dürften**	**sollten**	**wollten**	**wären**
ihr	**könntet**	**müsstet**	**dürftet**	**solltet**	**wolltet**	**wär(e)t**
sie, Sie	**könnten**	**müssten**	**dürften**	**sollten**	**wollten**	**wären**

A. Fill in each blank with the correct subjunctive form of **können**.

1. Du **könntest** mich wirklich einmal anrufen. Du hast doch ein Handy!
2. Wir ____________________ einen Ausflug machen, wenn wir mehr Zeit hätten.
3. Ihr ____________________ uns wirklich einmal eine E-Mail schicken.
4. Deine Eltern ____________________ doch die Gebühr für dein Handy zahlen.
5. Ich ____________________ dir eigentlich meine neue E-Mail-Adresse schicken.
6. Wer ____________________ mir die Hausaufgaben e-mailen?
7. Brad, das ____________________ du doch wirklich für mich tun.
8. Ich ____________________ mich mal so richtig aufs Wochenende freuen.

B. Fill in each blank with the correct **wäre**-form.

1. Ich wollte, ich ___**wäre**___ nicht so müde.
2. Ich wollte, du ________________ ein bisschen schneller.
3. Ich wollte, deine Schwester ________________ genauso fleißig wie du.
4. Ich wollte, wir ________________ nächsten Sommer an der Ostseeküste.
5. Ich wollte, ihr ________________ bereit, mit uns zu reisen.
6. Ich wollte, deine Eltern ________________ besser bekannt mit meinen Eltern.
7. Ich wollte, ich ________________ in einem guten Foto-Klub.

C. Write the following sentences in German, using subjunctive forms of modals.

1. I wish I could send you an e-mail.

   Ich wollte, ich könnte dir eine E-Mail schicken.

2. I would have to buy a computer first.

   ____

3. But you could send me an e-mail.

   ____

4. What could I do for you?

   ____

5. You could buy me a cell phone.

   ____

6. A cell phone should not cost more than 40 euros.

   ____

7. I wish I were in the mountains.

   ____

D. Summarize what you have learned about the subjunctive forms of the modals and **sein**.

____

____

THE PASSIVE VOICE

In English The **voice** of a verb refers to whether the subject is performing the action of the verb, or whether the subject is being acted upon. Verbs can be grouped into two categories: **active voice** and **passive voice**.

a. **Active voice** means that the grammatical subject of the sentence is performing or causing the action expressed by the verb.

Most people recycle paper and glass.

b. **Passive voice** means that the grammatical subject of the sentence is the recipient of the action or effect of the verb.

Paper and glass **are being recycled** by most people.

c. In the **passive voice**, a form of **to be** is used with the **past participle** of the main verb.

Present tense	The library **is used** by many people.
Imperfect	The clock **was repaired** only the day before yesterday.
Present Perfect	This movie **has been seen** by all the students.

d. Modals can also be used in the passive voice.

Present tense	This movie **can be seen** by younger students, too.
Imperfect	This film **could** not **have been shown** abroad.

A. Underline the passive verb construction in each of the following sentences.

1. I didn't know that this magazine <u>was read</u> by so many people.
2. Beer and soft drink cans are being recycled in almost every community.
3. My picture is being taken tomorrow.
4. Did you know that my car is being worked on this afternoon?
5. This new film is being introduced today nationwide.
6. Do you remember where this movie was filmed?

In German German also categorizes verb forms as either **active voice** or **passive voice**.

a. **active voice**: the grammatical subject is performing or causing the action expressed by the verb

Die Schüler **sammeln** an unserer Schule Papier und Alu-Dosen.

b. **passive voice**: the grammatical subject is the recipient of the action expressed by the verb

Papier und Alu-Dosen **werden** von den Schülern an unserer Schule **gesammelt**.

c. In the **passive voice**, a verb form of **werden** is used with the **past participle** of the main verb.

Present tense	Die Bücherei **wird** von vielen Leuten **benutzt**.
Imperfect	Das Auto **wurde** erst vorgestern **repariert**.
Present Perfect	Dieser Film **ist** von allen Schülern **gesehen worden**.

d. Modals can also be used in the passive voice.

Present tense	Dieser Film **kann** auch von jüngeren Schülern **gesehen werden**.
Imperfect	Der Film **konnte** im Ausland nicht **gezeigt werden**.

e. In general, the passive voice is used in general statements when it does not matter who does the action or even if an actor is known.

Viel Papier **wird** heute aus Altpapier **gemacht**.
In Stuttgart und in München **werden** Autos **hergestellt**.

d. If the performer of the action is known and if you want to name the performer, the preposition **von** (in English *by*) is used with the **dative case** form.

Das Papier wird **von den** Schüler**n** gesammelt.
Dieser Film kann auch **von** jünger**en** Kinder**n** gesehen werden.

B. Fill in each blank with the correct passive construction. Use the present tense.

1. (zeigen) Ein Film über die Umwelt **wird** heute **gezeigt** .
2. (machen) Das Papier für unsere Bücher ____________ aus Altpapier ______________ .
3. (sammeln) Bei uns ____________ jetzt alle Batterien ______________ .
4. (wählen) Am Wochenende ____________ ein neuer Präsident ______________ .
5. (gießen) Diese Blumen ____________ einmal in der Woche ______________ .
6. (einladen) Alle Freunde ____________ zu dieser Fete ______________ .

C. Write questions in the passive voice, using the present tense and the words in parentheses.

1. Wann (das Licht ausmachen) **wird das Licht ausgemacht** ?
2. Wo (Alu-Dosen wieder verwerten) ______________________________ ?
3. Wann (der Müll zum Container bringen) ______________________________ ?
4. Warum (der Abfall wegwerfen) ______________________________ ?
5. Wann (dein Auto waschen) ______________________________ ?
6. Warum (die Läden heute schließen) ______________________________ ?

D. Complete each of the following sentences using the verbs in parentheses in the passive voice, present tense, and fill in the other blanks with the correct endings.

1. (lesen) Diese Bücher **werden** von alle**n** Kinder**n** **gelesen** .
2. (tragen) Diese Klamotten _________ von viele___ Jugendliche___ ______________ .
3. (spielen) Dieser Film _________ von zwei alt___ Männer___ ______________ .
4. (essen) Der Spinat _________ von ein___ klein___ Kind ______________ .
5. (trinken) Dieses Wasser _________ von einige___ klein___ Tieren ______________ .

E. Summarize what you have learned about the passive voice.

____

KAPITEL 9

CONDITIONAL SENTENCES (CONTINUED)

In English The **conditional** is a construction used instead of or together with the subjunctive. This construction uses ***would*** and the infinitive form without *to.* You use the conditional in:

a. polite requests: **Would** you please **show** me your cell phone?

b. in so-called "if ... then" statements

If we **had** time, we **would go** to the movies.

c. "If... then" statements can refer to present time. In such instances, you use subjunctive verb forms such as **had** or **were**.

CONDITION	CONCLUSION
If we **had** time (now),	we **would go** to the movies.
If I **were** in Munich (now),	I **would go** to Oktoberfest.

d. "If... then" statements can also refer to past time. In such instances, you use the **past conditional**, **would have + the verb**, in the conclusion.

If we **had had time**, we **would have gone** to the movies.
If I **had been** in Munich, I **would have gone** to Oktoberfest.

A. Rewrite the following sentences in the past tense.

1. If I had the patience, I would sit through the performance.

   If I had had the patience, I would have sat through the performance.

2. If we had the money, we would buy you a computer.

   ____

3. If our dad broke his leg, he would go to Dr. Gutbein to have it fixed.

   ____

4. I would not go to school if I had a cold as bad as yours.

   ____

5. Mom would not cook tonight if she didn't buy a chicken.

   ____

6. If she had plenty of groceries in the house, she would not go shopping.

   ____

In German The **conditional** in German is used much the same way as in English. The conditional is used in:

a. polite requests: **Würdest** du mir bitte dein Handy zeigen?

b. "if ... then" statements: Wenn wir Zeit **hätten**, **würden** wir ins Kino gehen.

c. "If ... then" statements can refer to present time. In such instances, you use verb forms such as **hätte**, **wäre**, **würde**.

CONDITION	CONCLUSION
Wenn wir (jetzt) Zeit **hätten**,	**würden** wir ins Kino gehen.
Wenn ich (jetzt) in München **wäre**,	**würde** ich aufs Oktoberfest gehen.

d. "If ... then" statements can also refer to past time. In such instances you use the **past conditional**: **hätte** or **wäre** + the **past participle** of the verb in both clauses.

CONDITION	CONCLUSION
Wenn wir Zeit **gehabt hätten**,	**hätten** wir einen tollen Film **gesehen**.
Wenn ich in München **gewesen wäre**,	**wäre** ich aufs Oktoberfest **gegangen**.

e. Conditional sentences can start with the conclusion, followed by the **wenn**-clause.

Wir **würden** gern an die Nordsee **fahren**, wenn wir längere Ferien **hätten**.
Ich **wäre** aufs Oktoberfest **gegangen**, wenn ich in München **gewesen wäre**.

B. Fill in each blank with the correct subjunctive form of **haben**, **sein**, or **werden**.

1. Wenn mein Vater mehr Geld **hätte**, **würde** er eine Reise machen.
2. Wenn ich kein Geld ______________, ______________ ich zu Hause bleiben.
3. Wenn Mike in Berlin ______________, ______________ er sich den Reichstag ansehen.
4. Wenn die Kinder am Wasser ______________, ______________ sie sich sehr freuen.
5. Wenn Holly älter ______________, ______________ sie einen besseren Job haben.

C. Rewrite each of the conditional clauses referring to the present as conditional clauses referring to the past.

1. Wenn wir Hunger hätten, würden wir etwas essen.

   Wenn wir Hunger gehabt hätten, hätten wir etwas gegessen.
2. Wenn ich schlauer wäre, würde ich auch Chinesisch lernen.

   ____
3. Wenn ich mehr Zeit hätte, würde ich an die Ostsee fahren.

   ____
4. Wenn die Schüler hungrig wären, würden sie in einen Imbissladen gehen.

   ____
5. Wenn du älter wärest, würdest du zur Bundeswehr gehen.

   ____
6. Wenn Jonathan ein Auto hätte, würde er mit uns an den Strand fahren.

   ____

KAPITEL 9

D. Summarize what you have learned about conditional clauses.

____

KAPITEL 10

PASSIVE VOICE (SUMMARY)

Pupil's Edition, p. 281

Compare In both English and German the **passive voice** is used in **different tenses**.

As you compare these sentences, note the following:

a. The past participle of the main verb is used in all tenses, even in the present tense.

b. The perfect tenses use the verb **sein** together with **worden**, the shortened form of **geworden** (the past participle of **werden**).

weak and strong verbs:

PRESENT	Das Auto **wird** heute **repariert**.	The car ***is being repaired*** today.
IMPERFECT	Das Auto **wurde** heute **repariert**.	The car ***was repaired*** today.
PERFECT	Das Auto **ist** einmal **repariert worden**.	The car ***has been repaired*** once.
FUTURE	Das Auto **wird** heute **repariert werden**.	The car ***will be repaired*** today.

with modal verbs:

PRESENT	Das Auto **muss repariert werden**!	The car ***must be repaired***!
IMPERFECT	Das Auto **musste repariert werden**.	The car ***had to be repaired***.

with modal verbs in the subjunctive:

PRESENT	Das Auto **könnte repariert werden**.	The car ***could be repaired***.
	Das Auto **sollte repariert werden**.	The car ***should be repaired***.
	Das Auto **müsste repariert werden**.	The car ***should be repaired***.

c. If you want to name the agent performing the action expressed by the verb, use **von** and the dative case.

The car was repaired ***by*** an excellent mechanic.
Das Auto wurde **von** ein**em** ausgezeichnet**en** Mechaniker repariert.

d. German uses an impersonal passive construction, especially in negative commands.

Hier **wird** nicht **geraucht**. Hier **wird** nicht **gesprochen**.

e. German uses the pronoun **es** to introduce short sentences in the passive.

Es wird in diesem Lokal viel geraucht. *oder*
In diesem Lokal wird viel geraucht.

A. Complete each sentence with the correct construction of the passive voice in the present tense.

1. (feiern) Sein Geburtstag **wird** am 3. Oktober **gefeiert**.
2. (zeigen) Diese Filme ____________ in Deutschland nicht ____________.
3. (spielen) Das Theaterstück ____________ in Berlin ____________.
4. (verkaufen) Die Tickets ____________ schon jetzt ____________.
5. (aufführen) „Der Rosenkavlier" ____________ in München ____________.
6. (begrüßen) Die Musiker ____________ mit lautem Klatschen ____________.
7. (geben) Ein Blumenstrauß ____________ dem Dirigenten ____________.

B. Rewrite the following sentences in the present perfect tense.

1. Dieser Film wird nicht gezeigt. **Dieser Film ist nicht gezeigt worden.**
2. Das Stück wird nicht gespielt. ______________________
3. Die Halle wird heute repariert. ______________________
4. Ich werde nicht gefragt. ______________________
5. Wir werden nicht gefilmt. ______________________
6. Ich werde wieder fotografiert. ______________________
7. Kurt wird nicht abgeholt. ______________________

C. Complete the following sentences by filling in the blanks with the correct passive form, present tense, of the verbs given.

1. (müssen / zeigen) Dieser Film **muss** unbedingt **gezeigt werden**.
2. (dürfen / sehen) Dieser Film __________ nicht __________.
3. (sollen / filmen) Dieser Film __________ in Bayern __________.
4. (wollen / stören) Der Schauspieler __________ nicht __________.
5. (können / finden) Meine Fotografien __________ nicht __________.
6. (müssen / verbieten) Die Vorstellung __________ für Kinder __________.

KAPITEL 10

D. Write the following sentences in the passive voice.

1. The table has to be repaired. **Der Tisch muss repariert werden.**
2. The table should be repaired. ______________________.
3. The table has been repaired. ______________________.
4. The table will be repaired. ______________________.
5. There is no smoking here. ______________________.
6. There is no speaking here. ______________________.
7. There is no dancing here. ______________________.

E. Summarize what you have learned about the passive voice.

____

____

____

FUTURE PERFECT AND PERFECT INFINITIVE *Pupil's Edition, p. 311*

In English The **future perfect** is a tense that expresses action completed by a specified time in the future. It is formed by using **will have** or **shall have** with a **past participle**

By age 50 I **will have retired** to Florida.
But first, at the age of twenty, I **will have completed** my computer training.

A. Rewrite each sentence in the future perfect.

1. They will receive many gifts when the baby is born.

   They will have received many gifts when the baby is born.

2. She will finish the paper by the end of the semester.

   ___

3. Dad will buy a new car by then.

   ___

4. I will go on vacation before Thanksgiving.

   ___

5. Katie will visit the park often.

   ___

In German As in English, the **future perfect tense** expresses action completed at a specific time in the future.The future perfect consists of a present-tense form of the verb **werden** or a modal verb, plus the **perfect infinitive** The perfect infinitive consisists of a **past participle** and the infinitive **haben** or **sein** (gemacht haben, gefahren sein).

a. The **perfect infinitive** can be used with **werden**

Wenn ich 30 Jahre alt bin, **werde** ich viel von der Welt **gesehen haben**
Wenn ich 40 Jahre alt bin, **werde** ich einmal um die Welt **geflogen sein**

b. The perfect infinitive can also be used with the modal verbs.

Ich **möchte** einmal in China **gewohnt haben**

B. In the following sentences, determine what represents the future perfect. Then underline the helping verb and circle the perfect infinitive.

1. Ich möchte wissen, wann du dein Studium (beendet haben) wirst.
2. Wir wollen hören, wenn sie ihr erstes Geld verdient haben wird.
3. Wenn ich um die Welt gereist sein werde, werde ich dir schreiben.
4. Sie kann schon ihren Schulabschluss gemacht haben, wenn sie 18 Jahre sein wird.
5. Wenn er 25 Jahre sein wird, muss er sein Studium abgeschlossen haben.
6. Wenn er aus den Staaten zurückkommen wird, wird er sehr viel gesehen haben.
7. Wir werden die Zeitung lesen und werden uns sehr gut informiert haben.

C. Complete each of the following sentences in the future perfect.

1. (beginnen) Wenn ich 24 bin, möchte ich eine Karriere als Computerfachmann **begonnen haben**.
2. (kaufen) Wenn ich 28 bin, will ich mir schon mehrere tolle Autos ________________.
3. (reisen) Wenn ich 30 bin, werde ich schon dreimal um die Welt ________________.
4. (schreiben) Wenn ich 33 bin, möchte ich schon meinen ersten Roman ________________.
5. (anfangen) Wenn ich 40 bin, werde ich bestimmt schon eine politische Karriere ________________.
6. (haben) Wenn ich 50 bin, möchte ich schon fünf Jahre ein ruhiges Leben ________________.
7. (sein) Wenn ich 55 bin, möchte ich schon zweimal auf einer Safari in Afrika ________________.

D. Summarize what you have learned about the future perfect.

____

____

Komm mit! German 1

Answers

Answers

KAPITEL 1

QUESTIONS p. 1

	INTERROGATIVE	VERB
A. 1.	✓	
2.		✓
3.	✓	
4.	✓	
5.	✓	
6.		✓
7.		✓
8.	✓	
9.	✓	
10.		✓

	INTERROGATIVE	VERB
B. 1.	✓	
2.		✓
3.	✓	
4.	✓	
5.	✓	
6.		✓
7.		✓
8.	✓	
9.	✓	
10.		✓

	INTERROGATIVE	VERB
C. 1. Wie	✓	
2. Woher	✓	
3. Wie	✓	
4. Kommt		✓
5. Wer	✓	
6. Ist / Kommt		✓
7. Woher	✓	
8. Kommt / Ist		✓
9. woher	✓	
10. Kommt / Ist		✓

D. Answers will vary. Possible answers: Questions can begin with an interrogative or a verb. When a question begins with an interrogative, the verb follows. When a question begins with a verb, the subject follows.

NOUNS p. 3

A.
1. This is the teacher.
2. The boy is called Harry.
3. He lives in Miami, Florida.
4. He rides his bike to school.
5. His teacher is Mrs. Schmidt.
6. What is the capital of Florida?
7. Our teacher takes his car to school.
8. I take the bus, and sometimes I take my bike.
9. Christa is from Berlin.
10. She takes the subway to school.

B.
1. Das ist der Lehrer.
2. Der Junge heißt Holger.
3. Er wohnt in Potsdam, in Brandenburg.
4. Er kommt mit dem Rad zur Schule.
5. Wer ist das Mädchen?
6. Sie heißt Sonja und ist fünfzehn Jahre alt.
7. Die Mutter bringt mich mit dem Auto zur Schule.
8. Wie heißt die Hauptstadt von Brandenburg?
9. Die Hauptstadt von Brandenburg heißt Potsdam.
10. Die Deutschlehrerin kommt aus Hamburg.

C.
1. Potsdam
2. Lehrer
3. Junge
4. Jahre
5. Schule
6. Bus / Rad
7. Auto
8. Fuß
9. Hauptstadt
10. Sonja

D. Answers may vary. Possible answers: German nouns are always capitalized.

DEFINITE ARTICLES p. 5

A.
1. Marvin takes the subway to school.
2. The German teacher is from Berlin.
3. Where is the bike?
4. The girl is called Hannah.
5. How old is the boy?
6. When does the bus come?

B.	M.	F.	N.
1. Wann kommt (der) Bus?	✓		
2. Wie alt ist (das) Moped?			✓
3. Woher kommt (die) U-Bahn?		✓	
4. (Das) Auto ist schon alt.			✓
5. Wo ist (das) Rad?			✓
6. Wie heißt (die) Hauptstadt?		✓	
7. Und wie heißt (das) Bundesland?			✓
8. Woher kommt (der) Deutschlehrer?	✓		

9. Woher ist (die) Biologielehrerin? ___ ✓ ___
10. (Das) Mädchen heißt Anja. ___ ___ ✓

C. 1. das 2. das 3. der 4. der 5. die 6. die 7. Das 8. das 9. der

D. Answers will vary. Possible answers: The German definite articles are der, die, das. Der is used with masculine nouns, die with feminine and plural nouns, and das with neuter nouns.

SUBJECTS *p. 7*

A. 1. Where does the teacher live?
2. The girl is from Austria.
3. Where is Mr. Brown from?
4. The student lives in Liechtenstein.
5. Is Jenny riding her moped to school?
6. What is the capital of Germany?
7. Monika is already sixteen.
8. The teacher comes from Austria.
9. How old is Handan?
10. Is she from Turkey?

B. 1. Wie heißt der Junge?
2. Woher kommt die Deutschlehrerin?
3. Das Auto kommt aus Österreich.
4. Wie heißt die Hauptstadt von Deutschland?
5. Wie alt ist die Biologielehrerin?
6. Der Holger ist auch schon 14 Jahre alt.
7. Der Junge da heißt Stefan, nicht?
8. Der Deutschlehrer ist aus Hessen.
9. Woher ist Annika? Aus Bern?
10. Wo liegt die Hauptstadt von Bayern?

C. 1. das Mädchen 2. der Junge 3. die Hauptstadt 4. der Lehrer 5. die Lehrerin

D. Answers may vary. Possible answers: The subject is the person or thing that performs the action.

SUBJECT PRONOUNS AND THE VERB *TO BE* *p. 9*

A. 1. Steven is fifteen years old.
2. I am sixteen years old.
3. We are from Kentucky.
4. Where is Mary from?
5. She is from Virginia.
6. The biology teacher is from New York.
7. Where are you from, Kirsten?
8. Where are you from, Alex and Julia?
9. We are from Erfurt.
10. Is Stefan also from Erfurt?

B. 1. Stefan ist fünfzehn Jahre alt.
2. Ich bin sechzehn Jahre alt.
3. Wir sind aus Kentucky.
4. Woher ist Mary?
5. Ich glaube, sie ist aus Virginia.
6. Der Biologielehrer ist aus New York.
7. Woher bist du, Kirsten?
8. Woher seid ihr, Alex und Julia?
9. Wir kommen aus Erfurt.
10. Kommt der Stefan auch aus Erfurt?

C. Answers may vary. Possible answers: Subjects can be nouns or pronouns.

D. is, am, are

E. ist, bin, sind, bist, seid

F. 1. Wir sind aus Michigan. Und woher seid **ihr**?
2. Mark ist aus Wisconsin und **er** ist 16 Jahre alt.
3. Barbara ist aus Idaho und **sie** ist schon 17 Jahre alt.
4. Dylan und James sind aus Texas; **sie** sind aus Plano.
5. Rick und Abe sind aus Arkansas; **sie** sind aus Little Rock.
6. Ich bin aus Illinois. Und woher bist **du** ?
7. Du bist aus Los Angeles und **ich** bin aus Milwaukee.
8. Ihr seid aus New York und **wir** sind aus New Jersey.

G. Answers will vary. Possible answers: The verb sein has five different forms: bin, bist, ist, sind, seid.

KAPITEL 2

SUBJECTS AND VERBS *p. 11*

A. 1. We listen to a lot of music.
2. Tara is not home.
3. She swims in the afternoon.
4. You collect stamps?
5. No, I collect comics.

6. Adam and Susan watch TV in the evening.
7. In the fall I hike a lot.
8. I play guitar and piano.
9. We hike on weekends.
10. I read a lot.

B. 1. Wir hören viel Musik.
2. Tara ist nicht zu Hause.
3. Sie schwimmt am Nachmittag.
4. Du sammelst Briefmarken?
5. Nein, ich sammle Comics.
6. Adam und Susan schauen am Abend Fernsehen.
7. Im Herbst wandre ich viel.
8. Ich spiele Gitarre und Klavier.
9. Wir wandern am Wochenende.
10. Ich lese viel.

C. Answers will vary. Possible answers: English has only one ending, -s. German has four: -e, -est, -t, -en.

CONJUGATION OF VERBS *p. 13*

A. 1. You (play) the piano, right?
2. Tara (plays) tennis very well.
3. Tara and Steffi (play) together often.
4. We (play) tennis only on the weekend.
5. The boys and girls (play) tennis together.
6. Holger (plays) tennis with his coach.
7. I (play) tennis whenever I can.

B. Two, for example: play, plays

C. 1. Du (spielst) Klavier, ja?
2. Tara (spielt) sehr gut Tennis.
3. Tara und Steffi (spielen) oft.
4. Wir (spielen) Tennis am Wochenende.
5. Die Jungen und Mädchen (spielen) Tennis.
6. Holger (spielt) Tennis mit dem Trainer.
7. Ich (spiele) auch Tennis.

D. Four, for example: spiele, spielst, spielt, spielen

E. 1. **spielen** can be used with **wir**, **sie**
2. **spielt** can be used with **er**, **sie**, **es**, **ihr**
3. **spiele** can be used with **ich**
4. **spielst** can be used with **du**

F.

1. du	5. Sie
2. Ich / ich	6. ich / sie
3. ihr	7. ihr
4. Wir / wir	8. Wir / Wir

G. Answers will vary. Possible answers: German has four different verb endings, depending on the subject.

SUBJECT-VERB AGREEMENT *p. 15*

A.

	SINGULAR	PLURAL
1.		✓
2.		✓
3.	✓	
4.	✓	
5.		✓
6.	✓	
7.	✓	
8.	✓	

B.

	S.	P.
1. Jens und Ahmet (spielen) Karten.		✓
2. Sie (spielen) Mau-Mau.		✓
3. Was (machst) du in deiner Freizeit, Steffi?	✓	
4. Ich (sammle) Briefmarken.	✓	
5. Im Winter (laufen) wir viel Ski.		✓
6. Holger (hat) andere Interessen.	✓	
7. (Spielen) Sie Tennis, Herr Meyer?	✓	
8. Frau Meyer (schwimmt) gern.	✓	

C.

1. Sammelst	6. wandert
2. sammle	7. tanzt
3. spielt	8. Tanzt
4. Spielt	9. Hörst
5. wanderst	10. höre

D.

1. spielen	5. spielen
2. Wandert	6. macht
3. sammeln	7. besuchen
4. spielen	8. zeichnen

E.

1. spielt	5. zeichnet
2. spielen	6. zeichnen
3. hörst	7. Besuchst
4. hört	8. wand(e)re

F. Answers will vary. Possible answers: Singular subjects take singular verb forms, plural subjects take plural verb forms.

PERSON AND NUMBER *p. 17*

A. 3rd person singular, he plays

B. 1st person singular, **spiele**; 2nd person, **spielst / spielt**; 3rd person singular, **spielt**

C.

1. Ich spiele	5. Wir spielen
2. Du spielst	6. Sie spielen
3. Er spielt	7. Sie spielen
4. Sie spielt	

D. 1. machst du
2. Ich spiele
3. machen
4. Ich / spielen
5. macht
6. Er / sammelt
7. machst
8. ich/ ich spiele

E. Answers will vary. Possible answer: There are three persons: first, second, and third. There are singular verb forms and plural verb forms.

PRESENT TENSE *p. 19*

A. 1. I do visit friends on the weekend.
2. And you are playing soccer.
3. Steffi lives in Germany.
4. She does play tennis very well.
5. Holger finds tennis boring.
6. He is playing the guitar.
7. We do play soccer on the weekend.
8. Bobby and Rick, you are playing cards in the evening.
9. They also play volleyball on the weekend.
10. Taylor and I are playing chess.

B. 1. Ich besuche Freunde am Wochenende.
2. Und du spielst Fußball.
3. Steffi wohnt in Deutschland.
4. Sie spielt ja sehr gut Tennis.
5. Holger findet Tennis langweilig.
6. Er spielt Gitarre.
7. Wir spielen am Wochenende Fußball.
8. Bobby und Rick, ihr spielt Karten am Abend.
9. Sie spielen auch Volleyball am Wochenende.
10. Taylor und ich spielen Schach.

C. do visit, are playing, lives, does play, finds, is playing, do play, play

D. three: regular, progressive, emphatic

E. **besuche, spielst, wohnt, spielt, findet, spielen**

F. Answers will vary. Possible answer: German has only one present tense form. German does not have a progressive or an emphatic present tense.

WORD ORDER: POSITION OF THE VERB IN A STATEMENT *p. 21*

A. 1. We are playing soccer after school.
2. In the evening we are playing tennis.
3. After school I am doing my homework.
4. Holger does homework in the evening.
5. In the evening Mark and Matt watch television.
6. In the fall we hike a lot.

B. 1. The subject is immediately before the verb.
2. a time expression

C. 1. Wir spielen nach der Schule Fußball.
2. Am Abend spielen wir Tennis.
3. Tennis spielen wir am Abend.
4. Nach der Schule mache ich Hausaufgaben.
5. Holger macht die Hausaufgaben am Abend.
6. Am Abend schauen Mark und Matt Fernsehen.
7. Im Herbst wandern wir viel.
8. Die Schüler finden Deutsch einfach.

D. 1. It's either directly before or directly after the verb.
2. the verb

E. 1. Ich jogge *am Nachmittag*.
Am Nachmittag jogge ich.
2. Wir spielen *im Sommer* Tennis.
Im Sommer spielen wir Tennis.
3. Wir finden *Deutsch* einfach.
Deutsch finden wir einfach.
4. Sabine hört *am Abend* Musik.
Am Abend hört Sabine Musik.
5. Ich spiele *nach der Schule* Klavier.
Nach der Schule spiele ich Klavier.
6. Wir spielen nach der Schule *Golf*.
Golf spielen wir nach der Schule.
7. Ich finde *Tennis* super.
Tennis finde ich super.
8. Wir wandern gern *im Herbst*.
Im Herbst wandern wir gern.

F. 1. any element: an interrogative, the subject, any other expression (an expression of time or place)
2. in second position
3. in first or third position
4. when another element is in first position

G. Answers will vary. Possible answer: Any element (subject, expression of time, etc.) can begin a sentence. The verb must follow, then the subject.

KAPITEL 3

MODAL VERBS: THE MÖCHTE-FORMS *p. 23*

A. 1. Juan would eat a piece of cake.
2. Katie may have fruit.
3. We can drink a glass of orange juice.
4. I must drink apple juice.
5. Holger may visit his friend.
6. Steffi should drink a cola.
7. Jens and Steffi would take a few cookies.
8. Mr. Moser could live in the country.
9. We might visit friends.
10. I should buy the car.

B. 1. Holger möchte ein Stück Kuchen essen.
2. Möchtest du eine Limo trinken?
3. Wir möchten ein Glas Orangensaft trinken.
4. Was möchte Holger essen?
5. Holger möchte ein paar Kekse essen.
6. Steffi möchte eine Cola trinken.
7. Jens und ich möchten ein paar Kekse.
8. Herr Moser möchte auf dem Land wohnen.
9. Möchte Inge Freunde besuchen?
10. Ich möchte das Auto.

C. 1. möchtest
2. möchte
3. möchtet
4. möchten
5. möchte
6. möchte
7. möchten
8. möchte
9. Möchtest
10. möchtet

D. first or second/ last

E. Answers will vary. Possible answer: The endings are **-e, -est, -et, -en**. The first- and third-person singular forms are the same. Modals can be used with other verbs.

THIRD-PERSON PRONOUNS *p. 25*

A. 1. What is the boy called? – He is called Ahmet.
2. How old is the armoire? – It is forty years old.
3. How big is the shelf? – It is not very big.
4. Is the couch new? – Yes, it is new, quite new.
5. Is Mrs. Weigel the biology teacher? – Yes, she is the biology teacher.
6. Is the apple juice good? – Yes, it is good.

B. 1. Wie heißt der Junge? – Er heißt Ahmet.
2. Wie alt ist der Schrank? – Er ist vierzig Jahre alt.
3. Wie groß ist das Regal? – Es ist nicht sehr groß.
4. Ist die Couch neu? – Ja, sie ist neu, ganz neu.
5. Ist Frau Weigel die Biologielehrerin? – Ja, sie ist die Biologielehrerin.
6. Ist der Apfelsaft gut? – Ja, er ist gut.
7. Das Regal ist groß. – Ja, es ist sehr groß.
8. Der Stuhl ist sehr unbequem. – Ja, und er ist auch kaputt.
9. Ist der Computer neu? – Ja, er ist ganz neu.

C.

	MASCULINE	FEMININE	NEUTER	PLURAL
1.		✓		
2.				✓
3.	✓			
4.			✓	
5.				✓
6.	✓			
7.				✓
8.		✓		

D. 1. Ist die Couch im Zimmer? sie
2. Wie groß ist der Stuhl? er
3. Wo wohnen Jens und Holger? sie
4. Der Orangensaft ist nicht gut. er
5. Was macht denn die Tara? sie
6. Das Regal ist zu klein. es
7. Wo ist denn der Kuchen? er
8. Woher ist der Schreibtisch? er

E. Answers will vary. Possible answer: The third-person pronouns are **er, sie, es**. **Er** refers to a masculine noun, **sie** to a feminine or a plural noun, and **es** to a neuter noun.

KAPITEL 4

NOUNS AND THEIR PLURAL FORMS *p. 27*

A. 1. Two men have been playing tennis for the past two days.
2. There are more fish in the bay now than in 1980.
3. Books for children can be expensive.
4. Mice make cheap pets.
5. Several dignitaries are in the audience.
6. All of the money is invested in bonds.

B.	SINGULAR	PLURAL	BOTH
1.		✓	
2.	✓		
3.		✓	
4.			✓
5.		✓	
6.	✓		
7.		✓	
8.		✓	
9.			✓

C. 1. Holger hat ein Mädchen gern. (Mädchen) haben Holger gern.
2. Der Taschenrechner ist teuer. – Ja, (Taschenrechner) sind teuer.
3. Wie teuer sind (Bleistifte)? Und wie teuer ist das Heft?
4. (Meine Schwestern) heißen Cindy und Pam. Wie heißt deine Schwester?
5. Die Kassette kostet 1 Euro, und (die Kassetten) da kosten nur 50 (Cent).
6. (Die Wörterbücher) sind teuer, aber das Wörterbuch da ist preiswert.
7. Das Zimmer ist sehr schön, und (die Zimmer) da vorn sind super!
8. Mein Bruder ist 17, und Eriks (Brüder) sind schon 20 und 21 (Jahre) alt.

D. Anwers will vary. Possible answer: You must memorize the plural form of nouns.

KAPITEL 5

DIRECT OBJECTS *p. 29*

A. 1. That girl would like to buy (the sweater).
2. Is Mark buying (the shirt)?
3. No, my friend is buying (the shoes).
4. The shoes cost (80 euros).
5. The children also need (tennis shoes).
6. My brother will take (the sweater.)

B. 1. Ich brauche (eine Hose); die Hose hier sieht toll aus.
2. Ich suche (einen Pulli) in Braun; der Pulli hier ist nicht teuer.
3. Der Gürtel ist zu lang; ich brauche (einen Gürtel) – ja, aber in Schwarz, bitte.
4. Hier ist ein Gürtel in Schwarz, aber der Gürtel kostet (20 Euro).
5. Haben Sie (einen Wunsch)? – Ich brauche (Turnschuhe).
6. Die Bluse ist nicht teuer. Gut, ich kaufe (die Bluse).
7. Schau, der Taschenrechner ist billig. Ich brauche (einen Taschenrechner).
8. Suchst du (den Kuli)? – Nein, ich habe (den Kuli).

C. 1. den
2. die
3. das
4. den
5. das
6. die
7. den
8. den

D. 1. einen
2. eine
3. ein
4. einen
5. eine
6. ein
7. einen

E. Answers will vary. Possible answer: The accusative case of the articles is different only for masculine nouns: **der** changes to **den**, **ein** to **einen**.

SUBJECT AND DIRECT OBJECT (NOUN PHRASES) *p. 31*

A. 1. Do you have (the sweater) in black?
2. Isn't this belt awful?
3. I would like (a sweater) in blue, please.
4. I don't need (a jogging suit).
5. How do you like (my skirt)?
6. Your skirt looks great!
7. And your blouse is also cute!

B. 1. Ich finde (den Gürtel) ein bisschen zu kurz.
2. (Den Gürtel) finde ich auch zu teuer.
3. (Das Hemd) nehme ich; ich finde (das Hemd) einfach toll!
4. (Die Bluse) kaufe ich nicht. Die Bluse gefällt mir nicht.
5. Sie zieht nur (schwarze Klamotten) an. (Schwarze Klamotten) findet sie schick.
6. (Die Jeans) brauche ich nicht. Die Jeans ist auch zu groß.
7. Dein Rock ist ja super, und (deinen Gürtel) finde ich auch hübsch.

C.	SUGG. NOUNS	MASC.	FEM.	NEUT.
1.	Pulli	✓		
2.	Bluse		✓	
3.	Hemd			✓
4.	T-Shirt			✓
5.	Jacke		✓	
6.	Gürtel	✓		

D.
1. Die Jacke kaufe ich nicht.
2. Den Pulli finden wir stark
3. Die Stiefel zieht Rosi nicht an.
4. Den Rock finde ich echt stark.
5. Die Klamotten braucht Rosi nicht.
6. Die Turnschuhe suche ich.
7. Das T-Shirt findet Katja scheußlich.
8. Das Hemd findet Michael echt super.

E. Anwers will vary. Possible answer: Case allows you to place noun phrases in different positions.

DIRECT OBJECT PRONOUNS *p. 33*

A.
1. Does Scott like the sweater?
2. No, it doesn't suit him.
3. I find it cool.
4. Then you should buy it.
5. Do they have sweaters in red?
6. They only have them in black.
7. My sister visits her once a week.
8. My parents would like it in dark blue.

B.

1.	Hemd	Stiefel	Pulli	Bluse
2.	Jeans	Rock	T-Shirt	Pulli
3.	Kleid	Shorts	Jacke	Hemd
4.	Stiefel	Gürtel	Hose	Rock
5.	Gürtel	Jacke	Klamotten	T-Shirt
6.	Jacke	Hemd	T-Shirt	Pulli
7.	Jeans	Jacke	Hemd	Pulli
8.	Jacke	Gürtel	Pulli	Hemd
9.	Jacke	Hemd	Schuhe	Bluse
10.	Hose	Gürtel	Schuhe	Hemd

C.
1. sie
2. sie
3. ihn
4. es
5. sie
6. sie
7. es
8. sie
9. ihn
10. ihn

D. Answers will vary. Possible answer: The pronoun **ihn** is used to refer to masculine nouns, **sie** refers to feminine and plural nouns, and **es** refers to neuter nouns.

SEPARABLE-PREFIX VERBS *p. 35*

A.
1. Der Pulli sieht wirklich gut aus.
2. Ich finde den Pulli wirklich stark!
3. Warum probierst du die Hose nicht an?
4. Ich ziehe den Jogging-Anzug zur Fete an.
5. Sieht mein T-Shirt nicht fesch aus?
6. Ich kaufe die Bluse nicht.
7. Die Schuhe sehen toll aus, aber sie sind zu teuer.
8. Simone nimmt die Hose nicht.
9. Probierst du das Kleid oder den Rock an?
10. Die Stiefel sehen toll aus, nicht?

B.
1. ziehe / an
2. siehst / aus
3. probiert / an
4. ziehst / an
5. seht / aus
6. probiert / an
7. probieren / an
8. ziehen / an
9. sieht / aus
10. sieht / aus

C. Answers will vary. Possible answer: The prefix goes to the end of the sentence.

KAPITEL 6

WORD ORDER: EXPRESSIONS OF TIME AND PLACE *p. 37*

A.
1. We want to go to the disco at night.
2. I want to go to the mall in the morning.
3. Who wants to go to the pool at 10 o'clock?
4. Susan wants to go to the tennis court early in the morning.
5. Why do you want to go to Berlin in the winter?
6. We want to go to the mountains in the fall.
7. My parents want to fly to Germany in October.
8. But who does not want to go to the Oktoberfest in the fall?
9. Are you going to the café after school?
10. I would like to be at the airport by noon.

B.
1. Wir wollen nach der Schule in die Stadt gehen.
2. Wollt ihr am Abend ins Konzert gehen?
3. Der Johannes möchte am Nachmittag in ein Café gehen.
4. Ich will um vier Uhr ins Kino gehen.
5. Willst du jetzt ins Schwimmbad gehen?
6. Ich möchte nach der Mathestunde nach Hause gehen.
7. Meine Eltern fliegen im Winter nach Spanien.
8. Prima! Wer möchte nicht im Dezember nach Florida fliegen?
9. Brenna und Erik wollen am Wochenende ins Schwimmbad gehen.
10. Gregor, willst du um halb vier ins Café gehen?

C. 1. Ich möchte um Viertel nach neun in die Stadt fahren.
2. Wir wollen nach der Schule Fußball spielen.
3. Der Mike möchte danach ins Schwimmbad gehen.
4. Wollt ihr am Abend ins Kino gehen?
5. Meine Mutter möchte jetzt ins Einkaufszentrum fahren.
6. Die Jungen wollen um Viertel vor vier ins Café Freizeit gehen.
7. Wollt ihr heute ins Rockkonzert gehen?
8. Ich möchte nach der Biostunde nach Hause gehen.
9. Hans und Maria wollen am Wochenende in die Disko gehen.
10. Wir wollen Freitag nach Berlin fahren.

D. Answers will vary. Possible answers: Expressions of time precede expressions of place.

KAPITEL 7

SEPARABLE-PREFIX VERBS AND MODALS *p. 39*

A.

1. anprobieren	6. anziehen
2. abräumen	7. anprobieren
3. aussehen	8. anprobieren
4. aufräumen	9. mitkommen
5. mitkommen	10. abräumen

B. 1. Ich kann die Jacke nicht anprobieren.
2. Du musst die Stiefel anziehen.
3. Wer kann den Tisch abräumen?
4. Claudia muss die Klamotten aufräumen.
5. Wer kann mitkommen?
6. Ich muss zuerst die Schuhe anprobieren.
7. Marga will gut aussehen.
8. Jens und Lars möchten Jeans anziehen.
9. Max will den Tisch nicht abräumen.
10. Anna möchte die Schuhe anprobieren.

C. Answers will vary. Possible answer: In sentences with a modal verb, the infinitive is used. If the infinitive is a separable-prefix verb, the prefix is NOT separated.

OBJECT PRONOUNS: SECOND PERSON *p. 41*

A. 1. We'd like to see you in the afternoon.
2. Will you call us in the afternoon?
3. He might ask you out.
4. I find you very interesting.
5. Would you see me after class?
6. She needs her to set the table.
7. We'll visit her on the weekend.
8. Do you see him in the library?

B. 1. Ich besuche dich nach der Schule.
2. Wer möchte uns heute besuchen?
3. Ich möchte Sie etwas fragen, Herr Müller.
4. Warum brauchst du mich heute?
5. Wann wollt ihr uns einmal besuchen?
6. Ich finde dich einfach toll!
7. Ich besuche Sie heute nach der Schule.
8. Wir möchten euch gern etwas fragen.

C.

1. dich	5. dich
2. mich	6. uns / mich
3. uns	7. Sie
4. mich	8. euch

D. Answers will vary. Possible answer: First- and second-person pronouns have different forms.

KAPITEL 8

COMMAND FORMS: THE DU-COMMAND AND THE IHR-COMMAND *p. 43*

A. 1. I eat bread every day. Eat bread every day!
2. We watch TV and turn it off at 9 o'clock. Watch TV and turn it off at 9 o'clock.
3. Go home to read the newpaper. I go home to read the newspaper.
4. We'll take the money. Take the money.
5. Sort the garbage for your mother. I'll sort the garbage for your mother.
6. You tell good stories. Tell me when you're done.
7. Be at school at 7:30. No, you should be there at 7:20.
8. Clear the table today. We'll clear the table tomorrow.

B. 1. Kauf doch das Brot beim Bäcker, und du gehst jetzt zuerst zum Supermarkt, ja?
2. Räumt das Zimmer auf, und ihr sortiert den Müll!
3. Besuch zuerst die Oma, und geht dann zusammen einkaufen!
4. Macht zuerst die Hausaufgaben und schaut danach Fernsehen!
5. Rolf, frag den Biolehrer, und fragt den Deutschlehrer nach der Pause!
6. Geh ins Kino oder geh den Opa besuchen!

C. 1. Kauf die Wurst lieber beim Metzger und holt die Milch im Supermarkt!
2. Wiegt das Gemüse und zahlt nicht zu viel für das Obst!
3. Mach das Bett und räumt zusammen das Zimmer auf.
4. Sortiert zuerst den Müll und fahrt danach zusammen in die Stadt.
5. Kommt doch mit zum Bäcker, aber du, Holger, zieh zuerst dein Hemd an!
6. Bestell doch eine Pizza und trink eine Limo dazu.

D. 1. hol
2. kauft
3. vergesst
4. räum / auf
5. sortiert
6. mäh
7. macht

E. Answer will vary. Possible answer: The **du**-command uses the **du**-form of the present tense verb without the ending **-st** (or **-est**); the **ihr**-command uses the same form as the present tense. No pronouns are used.

■ SENTENCES AND CLAUSES *p. 45*

A. 1. We get our groceries at the supermarket because they are cheaper there.
2. I like to eat vegetables because they are good for me.
3. My father listens to classical music because he likes it better than anything else.
4. I can't play soccer today because I have no time.
5. Jenna must do her homework more diligently because she needs better grades.
6. Mom must clean the house because my grandparents are coming to see us.
7. Traffic is heavy because it is 5:00.
8. Because flooding at the lake is ongoing, we can't vacation there this year.

B. 1. Ich gehe nicht schwimmen, weil ich meine Hausaufgaben machen muss.
2. Julia kann den Pulli nicht kaufen, denn sie hat kein Geld.
3. Wir waren nicht beim Bäcker, weil wir noch Brot zu Hause haben.
4. Ein deutsches Pfund wiegt mehr, weil es 500 Gramm hat.
5. Ich möchte noch ein Ei, denn ich habe Hunger.
6. Wir gehen nicht ins Kino, weil wir erst letzte Woche im Kino waren.
7. Du musst einkaufen gehen, denn du brauchst neue Klamotten.
8. Die Mutti kann heute nicht zum Supermarkt fahren, weil sie keine Zeit hat.

C. 1. Ich gehe zum Metzger, weil ich Fleisch und Wurst kaufen muss.
2. Wir können heute nicht Tennis spielen, denn wir haben keine Zeit.
3. Sean muss zu Hause helfen, weil seine Schwester etwas anderes machen muss.
4. Ich hab das Brot beim Bäcker gekauft, denn es ist dort immer frisch.
5. Ich kann dir nicht helfen, weil ich zu Hause so viel zu tun habe.
6. Ihr müsst zu Hause bleiben, weil ihr den Müll noch nicht sortiert habt.
7. Wir können dich heute Abend nicht anrufen, denn wir sind alle bei den Großeltern.
8. Ich soll heute ins Kino gehen, weil es dort einen guten Film gibt.

D. Answers will vary. Possible answer: In **weil**-clauses the verb is in last position, in **denn**-clauses the verb is in second position.

KAPITEL 9

■ FORMAL SIE-COMMAND *p. 47*

A.

	DU	IHR	SIE
1.	✓		
2.			✓
3.		✓	
4.			✓
5.	✓		
6.		✓	
7.	✓		
8.			✓

9.		✓	
10.	✓		

B. 1. Gehen Sie doch nach Hause.
2. Fahren Sie bis zur Ampel.
3. Trinken Sie mal ein Mineralwasser.
4. Sortieren Sie den Müll.
5. Kaufen Sie das Brot beim Bäcker.
6. Fragen Sie mal die Schüler.
7. Fahren Sie bitte nicht so schnell.
8. Warten Sie auf mich am Rathaus.
9. Kommen Sie doch mit.
10. Füttern Sie bitte die Katze für mich.

C. 1. Schreiben Sie bitte das Wort an die Tafel.
2. Buchstabieren Sie bitte das Wort.
3. Sprechen Sie bitte langsam.
4. Geben Sie bitte den Test morgen.
5. Rufen Sie bitte die Eltern heute Abend an.
6. Warten Sie bitte im Schulhof.

D. Answers will vary. Possible answer: The **Sie**-command uses the **Sie**-form of the verb: the verb form comes first, followed by **Sie**.

THERE IS, THERE ARE *p. 49*

A.

1. There is	6. there is
2. There are	7. There are
3. There are	8. There is
4. there is	9. There is
5. There are	10. There are

B.

1. Es gibt	6. gibt es
2. es / gibt	7. gibt es
3. gibt es	8. Gibt es
4. Es gibt	9. gibt es
5. Es gibt	10. es gibt

C. Answers will vary. Possible answers: Es gibt can refer to singular or plural nouns.

NEGATION: NICHT AND KEIN *p. 51*

A. 1. I don't eat the cake because I'm not hungry.
2. I have no money, and I cannot go to Berlin.
3. I cannot play tennis because I have no time.
4. I don't know where the station is. I have no idea.
5. We are not vegetarians, but we eat no meat.
6. I have no car, and I cannot come to see you.

B. no money, no time, no idea, no meat, no car / a noun

C. 1. Ich esse den Kuchen nicht, weil ich keinen Hunger habe.
2. Ich habe kein Geld und kann nicht nach Berlin fahren.
3. Ich kann nicht Tennis spielen, weil ich keine Zeit habe.
4. Ich weiß nicht, wo der Bahnhof ist. Ich habe keine Ahnung.
5. Ich kann den Saft nicht trinken, weil ich keinen Durst habe.
6. Wir haben kein Brot, weil ich nicht einkaufen war.
7. Wir können nicht in die Disko gehen, weil wir kein Geld haben.
8. Wir essen keine Wurst mehr, weil wir nicht wissen, was in der Wurst ist.

D.

	NICHT	KEIN
1.	✓	
2.		✓
3.		✓
4.	✓	
5.		✓
6.		✓
7.	✓	

E. 1. Ich weiß nicht, wo der Marktplatz ist.
2. Ich habe jetzt keine Zeit.
3. Ich esse nicht, weil ich keinen Hunger habe.
4. Ich esse keine Wurst, weil ich sie nicht mag.
5. Ich weiß nicht, warum du keinen Spinat isst!
6. Sag, warum du keine Zeit hast!
7. Wir haben keinen Garten.
8. Ich warte nicht am Marktplatz.

F. Answers will vary. Possible answer: You use **nicht** with verbs and adjectives, and **kein** with nouns, to make negative statements.

KAPITEL 11

INDIRECT OBJECTS *p. 53*

A.
1. Andreas gives Martin a glass of juice.
2. Nicole buys him a beautiful birthday cake.
3. Will you tell me a story?
4. Pass your father a roll.
5. I sent him the bill last week.
6. You should offer the old lady your seat.
7. My mother gave me the flu.
8. Julia presented the winner a trophy.
9. The mechanic gave my car a tune-up.
10. Could you please bring me a book?

B.
1. Ich habe meiner Mutti Blumen gekauft.
2. Meinem Vati habe ich Pralinen gekauft, und ich habe ihm auch Blumen geschenkt.
3. Meinen Freunden kaufe ich CDs zum Geburtstag.
4. Wir kaufen den Eltern ein Handy, und wir geben ihnen auch zwei Telefonkarten.
5. Dem Martin gebe ich Pralinen, und ich schenke ihm auch einen Kalender.
6. Meiner Freundin schenke ich ein Video, und ich gebe ihr auch ein Buch.

C.
1. Unseren Eltern schenken wir eine CD.
2. Meinem Bruder schenke ich ein Buch.
3. Meiner Schwester schenke ich ein Handy.
4. Dem Vater schenken wir ein Sachbuch.
5. Der Mutter schenke ich eine Telefonkarte.
6. Den Jungen schenken wir Klamotten.
7. Den Großeltern schenkt Alex ein Video.
8. Meiner Freundin kaufe ich Pralinen.
9. Meiner Tante gebe ich einen Blumenstrauß.
10. Dem Lehrer schenken wir einen Kuli.

D. Answers will vary. Possible answer: Indirect objects are in the dative case. They can begin a sentence when emphasis on the indirect object is intended.

KAPITEL 12

TO KNOW (SUMMARY) *p. 55*

A.
1. kenne
2. kann
3. weiß
4. wissen
5. kennt
6. weiß / kennt
7. wissen / kann
8. kennt / weiß
9. weiß / kann
10. kennen / wissen / kann

B. Answers will vary. Possible answers: **Wissen** means to know a fact or information; **kennen** means to know or be acquainted with something; **können** means to know a language or a skill.

MOOD AND MODAL VERBS (SUMMARY) *p. 56*

A.
1. Wir können den Müll sortieren.
2. Wir wollen den Müll sortieren.
3. Wir sollen den Müll sortieren.
4. Wir möchten den Müll sortieren.
5. Wir müssen den Müll sortieren.
6. Wir dürfen heute den Müll sortieren.

B.
1. Ich will den Film nicht sehen.
2. Ich möchte den Film nicht sehen.
3. Ich muss den Film nicht sehen.
4. Ich soll den Film nicht sehen.
5. Ich kann den Film nicht sehen.
6. Wir dürfen den Film nicht sehen.

MODAL VERBS (A SUMMARY) *p. 57*

A. 1. Wir möchten heute mal die Stadt besichtigen.
2. Wollt ihr nicht lieber in den Zoo gehen?
3. Ich soll zu Hause bleiben. Ich muss meinen Eltern helfen.
4. Warum kannst du das nicht morgen tun?
5. Ich muss morgen die Garage aufräumen.
6. Willst du denn überhaupt nicht mehr mit uns weggehen?
7. Warum wollt ihr nicht mit uns ins Kino gehen?
8. Ich muss heute meine Hausaufgaben machen.

B. 1. kann
2. willst
3. müsst
4. sollen
5. will
6. möchtest
7. könnt
8. sollt

C. 1. Dürfen / gehen
2. kann / kaufen
3. will / anrufen
4. möchtest / sagen
5. will einladen
6. müsst / machen

D. Answers will vary. Possible answer: Modal verbs are usually used together with an infinitive. They can be used by themselves if the meaning is clear. With the exception of **möchte**, the modals have no endings in the first- and third-person singular. All other forms have regular verb endings. The modals **können, müssen,** and **wollen** have a vowel change in the present-tense forms.

Komm mit! German 2

Answers

Answers

KAPITEL 1 (WIEDERHOLUNG)

VERBS, PRESENT TENSE (REVIEW) *p. 61*

A. 1. You are not playing soccer on the weekend?
2. Yes, I do play soccer on the weekend.
3. Where are you spending your vacation?
4. We are going to Austria, to the mountains.
5. My grandparents live in Salzburg.
6. We are visiting them next summer.
7. My sister plays chess very well.
8. Sometimes I play with her, and then I lose.

B. 1. **st**
2. e
3. t
4. en
5. t
6. en
7. est
8. e

C. 1. **kommst**
2. glaube
3. probiert
4. habe
5. besichtigt
6. kennen
7. holst
8. brauche
9. hast
10. bist

D. 1. **gibt**
2. gibt
3. weiß
4. weißt
5. läufst
6. läuft
7. fährst
8. fährt/ fahre
9. habt

E. 1. **Was machst du?**
2. Ich spiele Karten.
3. Spielt Mike Karten?
4. Nein, aber er spielt Schach.
5. Was liest du?
6. Ich lese ein Buch.
7. Schreibst du eine E-Mail?
8. Ja, ich schreibe Mutti eine E-Mail.
9. Du schreibst viel!

KAPITEL 2 (WIEDERHOLUNG)

MODAL VERBS (REVIEW) *p. 63*

A. 1. **musst**
2. dürfen
3. könnt
4. will
5. sollen
6. möchtest
7. willst
8. muss
9. kann

B. 1. **Die Kinder dürfen kein Eis essen.**
2. Ich will die Jeans anziehen.
3. Du kannst mich später anrufen.
4. John muss den Rasen mähen.
5. Ihr möchtet ins Kino gehen.
6. Jennie soll den Kuchen kaufen.
7. Du musst viel Obst essen.
8. Möchtest du Saft trinken?

C. 1. **Wir müssen jetzt nach Hause gehen.**
2. Ich möchte um zwei Uhr essen.
3. Die Kinder dürfen Saft trinken.
4. Jenna will Schuhe kaufen.
5. Er soll nach Hause gehen.
6. Ich muss das Buch lesen.
7. Kannst du das glauben?
8. Sie möchte jetzt Tennis spielen.

MEANINGS OF MODAL VERBS (REVIEW) *p. 65*

A. 1. Wir können den Opa anrufen.
2. Wir wollen den Opa anrufen.
3. Wir sollen den Opa anrufen.
4. Wir möchten den Opa anrufen.
5. Wir müssen den Opa anrufen.
6. Wir dürfen den Opa anrufen.

B. 1. **Ich will nicht nach Hause gehen.**
2. Ich möchte nicht nach Hause gehen.
3. Ich muss nicht nach Hause gehen.
4. Ich soll nicht nach Hause gehen.
5. Ich kann nicht nach Hause gehen.
6. Wir dürfen nicht nach Hause gehen.

C. 1. **Er will heute Tennis spielen.**
2. Er möchte heute Tennis spielen.
3. Er muss heute Tennis spielen.
4. Er kann heute Tennis spielen.
5. Er soll heute Tennis spielen.
6. Wir dürfen heute Tennis spielen.

D. 1. **Ich möchte ins Kino gehen.**
2. Ich will *Gladiator* sehen.
3. Ich kann um 5 Uhr gehen.
4. Ich muss meine Hausaufgaben machen.
5. Kannst du Deutsch?
6. Ich kann Deutsch und Englisch.
7. Kannst du Schach spielen?
8. Warum musst du zu Hause bleiben?

SUBJECTS, DIRECT AND INDIRECT OBJECTS (REVIEW) *p. 67*

A.

S IO
1. My girlfriend bought her cousin
DO
a magazine subscription.

S IO
2. My cousin gave her sister
DO
a beautiful bracelet.

S IO DO
3. Michael lent his classmate ten euros.

S IO
4. Andrea wrote her grandparents
DO
a long letter.

S IO
5. My sister and I sent our cousins
DO
an e-mail.

S IO
6. Julia and Mark sent their math teacher
DO
a fax.

B.

S IO
1. Die Eltern haben meiner Schwester
DO
ein tolles Buch geschenkt.

DO S
2. Ein neues Auto hat der Vati gestern
IO
meiner Mutti gekauft.

IO S
3. Meinem Bruder hat die Mutti heute
DO
eine CD gegeben.

DO S
4. Eine E-Mail schicken die Kinder
IO
ihren Eltern heute.

IO S
5. Den Großeltern schicken die Eltern
DO
einen Blumenstrauß.

DO S
6. Was schenken denn deine Geschwister
IO
deinen Eltern zum Hochzeitstag?

IO
7. Dem neuen Deutschlehrer schenken
S DO
die Schüler einen Kalender.

DO
8. Und ein Buch über Bach schenken
S IO
die Musikschüler ihrem Musiklehrer.

IO S
9. Unserer Biolehrerin geben viele Schüler
DO
ein Buch über Tiere.

C. 1. **dem / einen**
2. der / einen
3. dem / einen
4. dem / eine
5. der / ein
6. der / ein
7. der / ein
8. dem / eine

D. 1. **ihn**
2. ihm
3. sie
4. ihr
5. ihn
6. ihn
7. ihr
8. ihm

KAPITEL 3

PAST TENSE p. 69

A.

	SIMPLE PAST	PRESENT PERFECT
1.	✓	
2.	✓	
3.		✓
4.		✓
5.		✓
6.	✓	
7.	✓	
8.		✓

B.

	SIMPLE PAST	PRESENT PERFECT
1.		✓
2.	✓	
3.		✓
4.		✓
5.		✓
6.		✓
7.	✓	

C. 1. **besucht**
2. gewohnt
3. gegessen
4. fotografiert
5. gespielt
6. gemacht
7. gefahren
8. gelesen
9. gegangen
10. gesehen

D. Answers will vary. Possible answers: There is simple past and the present perfect. The present perfect uses a form of **haben** or **sein** and a past participle of the main verb.

PAST PARTICIPLES p. 71

A. 1. We have hiked all over the Alps and have seen many interesting sights.
2. I have reminded you so often, and yet you still have not written that letter.
3. Have you hidden the presents you bought yesterday?
4. Daniel and Laura have already been to Munich, but they haven't visited Hamburg.
5. Pauline has acted as if my feelings don't matter.
6. I have worn that coat for so many years that I have become tired of it.
7. Have you received the package, or have you called about it?
8. I have cut the cake, but I haven't got enough forks.
9. I've already washed those pants, and they haven't shrunk.
10. Erika has given her allowance to charity instead of buying the toy she wanted.

B. 1. Am Nachmittag sind wir in die Stadt gegangen und haben Klamotten gekauft.
2. In den Ferien habe ich viel gegessen und gelesen.
3. Ich habe gehört, du hast deinem Freund Pralinen geschenkt.
4. Wir sind den ganzen Tag gelaufen und haben danach noch Tennis gespielt.
5. Ich habe ein Museum besichtigt und bin danach mit Mutti ins Kino gegangen.
6. Hast du ein gutes Buch gelesen, oder hast du nur gefaulenzt?

C. 1. Wir sind nach Bayern gefahren, und wir haben dort meine Großeltern besucht.
2. Ich habe viel gefilmt, und wir haben sehr viel gesehen.
3. Wir sind nach Garmisch gefahren und sind dort zwei Wochen geblieben.
4. Wir haben in einer Pension gewohnt und haben in tollen Lokalen gegessen.
5. Wir sind oft in den Bergen gewandert, und ich habe auch viel geschwommen.
6. Ich habe in den Bergen viel fotografiert, und ich habe tolle Dias gemacht.
7. Ich habe mir auch ein prima Buch gekauft und habe viel gelesen.

D. Answers will vary. Possible answer: Past participles of weak verbs end in **-t**, of strong verbs in **-en** or **-n**. You must memorize the past participles.

Answers

PRESENT PERFECT p. 73

A.
1. Have you seen the Schmidt's new car?
2. She has not yet heard if she won.
3. They have eaten the pizza, but they haven't drunk all the soda.
4. Whoever has left gum on the counter must clean it up.
5. I have read her other books, but I haven't heard about the latest one.
6. I found your letter, but I have not read it yet.
7. The Müllers have gone on vacation; they have flown to the coast of Spain.

B.
1. Wir sind nach Mittenwald gefahren und haben dort in einer Pension gewohnt.
2. Wo bist du in den Ferien gewesen und was hast du alles gemacht?
3. Ich bin zu Hause geblieben und habe gefaulenzt.
4. Hast du gehört, wer gekommen ist?
5. Wir haben Musik gespielt, und es ist sehr laut gewesen.
6. Wer hat denn gesehen, wann du einmal gearbeitet hast?

C.

	Change of Place	Direct Object
1.		✓
2.	✓	
3.		✓
4.	✓	
5.		✓
6.	✓	

D.
1. habe / gelesen
2. seid / gelaufen
3. hat / gemacht
4. bin / gefahren
5. habe / gefahren
6. bin / gewesen
7. sind / gegangen
8. haben / gesehen
9. hast / besucht

E. Answers will vary. Possible answer: The present perfect consists of a form of **haben** or **sein** and a past participle. All transitive verbs (verbs that can have a direct object) use **haben** and a past participle to form the present perfect; verbs that indicate a change of place or condition use **sein** and a past participle.

USE OF THE PRESENT PERFECT TENSE p. 75

A. *Mark und Sara*
1. Mark: **bin / gewesen**
2. Sara: seid / geblieben or gewesen
3. habt / gewohnt
4. Mark: haben / gewohnt
5. Sara: hast / gemacht
6. Mark: habe / gespielt
7. Sara: hast / gesehen
8. Mark: haben / besichtigt
9. Sara: bist / gewesen
10. Mark: sind / gewesen

Uhma und Clark

11. Uhma: **hast / gegessen**
12. Clark: sind / gegangen
13. Uhma: habt / gemacht
14. Clark: habe / gearbeitet
15. hat / sortiert
16. Uhma: habe / geholfen
17. habe / gespült
18. geputzt / bin / gegangen
19. Clark: bist / gewesen

B.
1. **Ich habe Tennis gespielt.**
2. Wir sind in die Stadt gegangen.
3. Wir haben einen Film gesehen.
4. Dann habe ich Freunde besucht.
5. Wir haben Karten gespielt.
6. Und wir haben eine Pizza gegessen.
7. Was hast du gemacht?
8. Ich habe ein Buch gelesen.
9. Ich habe das Magazin nicht gelesen.
10. Hast du das Buch gelesen?

C. Answers will vary. Possible answer: The present perfect is used in conversation when referring to past time, especially in the southern part of Germany and in Austria and Switzerland.

PREPOSITIONS: DIRECTION VS. LOCATION p. 77

A. 1. The squirrel ran up the tree and leapt onto the roof.
2. I'm going to the store – is there anything else I should write on the shopping list?
3. You'll have to see the pictures of our vacation to California.
4. Our house is past the park, near the big church.
5. I was at the movies with my friends.
6. Going through that experience was a turning point in my life.
7. If the cat isn't underneath the bed, try looking above the dryer.
8. Are we to make our beds before breakfast, or can we do without it this time?

B. 1. Wir waren schon im Gebirge, und jetzt fahren wir an die Nordsee.
2. Heute gehen wir ins Kino, denn gestern waren wir in der Oper.
3. Meine Mutter war eben im Garten. Ich glaube, sie ist in die Küche gegangen.
4. Warst du schon im Museum, oder gehst du jetzt erst ins Museum?
5. Ich war in der Türkei und fahre jetzt in die Schweiz.
6. Wann fährst du an die Nordsee? Ich war einmal an der Ostsee. Einfach toll!

C.

	LOCATION	DIRECTION
1.		✓
2.	✓	
3.	✓	
4.		✓
5.	✓	
6.	✓	
7.		✓
8.		✓

D. 1. **Wohin**
2. Wo
3. Wohin
4. Wo
5. Wo
6. Wohin
7. Wohin
8. Wo

E. Answers will vary. Possible answer: The prepositions **an, auf, in, über, unter, hinter, neben, vor,** and **zwischen** require objects to be in the dative case to express location, and in the accusative case to express direction.

INDIRECT OBJECT PRONOUNS p. 79

A. 1. We saw her in Frankfurt.
2. She invited us to go to a concert.
3. They bought me a very expensive ticket.
4. I gave them 5 euros.
5. How many times did they call you?
6. They called me five times.
7. When did you invite them for lunch?

B. 1. Wir haben sie angerufen, aber wir haben ihnen nicht im Garten geholfen.
2. Ich gebe euch gern das Buch, aber ich habe euch nicht gesehen.
3. Der Pulli hat ihr nicht gefallen, und sie hat ihn nicht gekauft.
4. Hast du ihr ein Geschenk gekauft, und hat sie dich nicht angerufen?
5. Ich habe ihm geschrieben, aber er hat mir nicht geantwortet.
6. Hast du sie gestern besucht, und hast du ihnen das Buch gegeben?
7. Kann ich Ihnen eine Zeitung geben, oder kann ich Sie sofort zum Chef bringen?
8. Warum hast du ihnen nicht geantwortet, als sie dich gerufen haben?
9. Ich habe dir das Buch geschenkt, weil es dir so gut gefallen hat.

C. 1. **ihm / dich**
2. Ihnen / Sie
3. ihr / sie
4. euch / euch
5. dich / dir
6. mir / dir
7. ihn / ihm

D. Answers will vary. Possible answer: Some object pronouns (mir, dir, etc.) are in the dative case. There are some verbs that require the direct object to be in the dative case, such as **denken**, **antworten**, and **gefallen**.

KAPITEL 4

REFLEXIVE PRONOUNS p. 81

A.
1. Don't blame yourself for losing the game.
2. He is congratulating himself for his three goals.
3. We pride ourselves in our success.
4. Did you cut yourself on the rock?
5. Martin forced himself to stay awake and finish his term paper.
6. Give yourselves a pat on the back!
7. The managers awarded themselves bonuses, even as the company went bankrupt.
8. Erika told herself that the party didn't matter anyway.
9. Hi, Max, help yourself to a soda!
10. The dog did itself a favor by leaving that snake alone.

B.
1. Wir waschen uns dreimal am Tag.
2. Ich schneide mich ab und zu in den Finger.
3. Und die Anja, sie schneidet sich nie.
4. Warum wäschst du dich nicht?
5. Wascht ihr euch nach dem Fußballspiel?
6. Der Max? Er wäscht sich immer nach dem Spiel.
7. Sag mal, wie hältst du dich fit?
8. Ich jogge und schwimme. So halte ich mich fit.

C.
1. dich
2. mich
3. sich
4. uns
5. euch
6. sich
7. sich

D. Answers will vary. Possible answer: The reflexive pronouns are mich, dich, sich, uns, and euch. They refer back to the subject.

REFLEXIVE VERBS p. 83

A.

	Personal Pronoun	Reflexive Pronoun
1.	✓	
2.		✓
3.	✓	
4.		✓
5.		✓
6.	✓	

B.
1. Ich frage dich, wie du dich fit hältst.
2. Wir fragen euch, wie ihr euch ernährt.
3. Darf ich Sie fragen, Herr Meier, wie Sie sich fühlen?
4. Du möchtest mich wohl fragen, wie ich mich ernähre.
5. Freut ihr euch nicht, dass ihr euch so wohl fühlt?
6. Ich freue mich, dass ihr euch so fit haltet.

C. sich fit halten sich ernähren, sich fühlen, sich freuen

D.
1. uns / euch
2. sich / uns
3. mich / dich
4. dich / dich
5. euch / euch
6. sich / sich

E.
1. Ich halte mich fit.
2. Wie hältst du dich fit?
3. Wir freuen uns nicht.
4. Ich fühle mich gut.
5. Fühlst du dich gut?
6. Er ernährt sich gut.
7. Ernährst du dich richtig?

F. Answers will vary. Possible answer: Reflexive verbs are listed like this: s. freuen. Reflexive verbs are used with reflexive pronouns.

KAPITEL 5

POSSESSIVE ADJECTIVES p. 85

A.
1. What do you have on your sandwich, John?
2. I have a piece of cheese on my sandwich.
3. Where did he buy his new car?
4. He bought his new car from a car dealer.
5. How did we get our car to run again?
6. They got their car to run again in no time.

Answers

B.

	Meaning	Gender	Case
1. Ich trinke meinen Kakao nicht.	**my**	**masc.**	**acc.**
2. Dein Pausenbrot sieht lecker aus.	your	neut.	nom.
3. Ich gebe die Milch seinem Bruder.	his	masc.	dat.
4. Sein Bruder trinkt Milch sehr gern.	his	masc.	nom.
5. Wo hast du meine Schwester gesehen?	my	fem.	acc.
6. Was hast du meiner Schwester gesagt?	my	fem.	dat.
7. Hast du schon ihr Auto gesehen?	her	neut.	acc.
8. Sein Rad war nicht sehr teuer.	his	neut.	nom.
9. Wo ist denn nur unser Fußball?	our	neut.	nom.

C.
1. **mein**
2. sein
3. unseren
4. ihren
5. ihrer
6. deinem
7. Ihren
8. ihre
9. unser

D. Answers will vary. Possible answer: Possesive adjectives (mein, dein, etc.) must agree in gender, number, and case with the noun being possessed.

KAPITEL 6

■ INCLUSIVE COMMAND p. 87

A.

	Regular	Inclusive
1.	✓	
2.		✓
3.		✓
4.	✓	
5.		✓
6.	✓	
7.	✓	
8.		✓

B.

	Statement	Inclusive Command
1.	✓	
2.		✓
3.	✓	
4.		✓
5.		✓
6.	✓	
7.	✓	
8.		✓

C.
1. **Rufen wir**
2. Gehen wir
3. Holen wir
4. Machen wir
5. Kaufen wir
6. Spielen wir
7. Fragen wir
8. Essen wir

D.
1. **Gehen wir zum Supermarkt!**
2. Rufen wir unsere Oma an!
3. Bleiben wir zu Hause!
4. Trinken wir Milch!
5. Gehen wir mit!
6. Lernen wir Deutsch!
7. Essen wir jetzt!
8. Sagen wir nichts!

E. Answers will vary. Possible answer: The inclusive command includes the speaker and uses the **wir**-form of the verb, with the pronoun following the verb: **Gehen wir!**

■ DIRECT OBJECTS IN THE DATIVE CASE p. 89

A.
1. Clayton, please answer the question.
2. I'll thank you with dinner tomorrow night.
3. What ails the boy?
4. We can follow you to the theater.
5. These jeans don't fit me anymore.
6. The shoes are too small; they hurt my feet.

B.

	Accusative	Dative
1.	✓	
2.		✓
3.	✓	
4.		✓
5.		✓
6.	✓	
7.		✓
8.	✓	
9.		✓
10.	✓	

Answers

C. 1. **deinem Opa**
2. deiner Oma
3. dir
4. ihm
5. der Renate
6. ihr
7. euch
8. meinem Bruder
9. deiner Mutter
10. dem Auto

D. 1. **Bobby, ich möchte dir helfen.**
2. Dieses Buch gehört mir.
3. Max, der Pulli passt dir gut.
4. Ich danke dir, Augustin.
5. Antworte mir, bitte!
6. Ihm gefällt das T-Shirt.
7. Mir gefällt es auch.
8. Wem gefällt das T-Shirt nicht?
9. Uns gefällt das T-Shirt nicht.

E. Answers will vary. Possible answer: There are a number of verbs in German that require the direct object to be in the dative case.

REFLEXIVE VERBS p. 91

A. 1. Habt ihr euch verletzt, oder habt ihr euch etwas gebrochen?
2. Hast du dich gewaschen, oder hast du dir nur die Füße gewaschen?
3. Er hat sich zuerst die Haare gewaschen, und dann hat er sich gewaschen.
4. Ich hab mich schwer verletzt; ich glaub, ich hab mir den Rücken verletzt.
5. Hast du dich verletzt, oder hast du dir sogar den Knöchel gebrochen?
6. Sie hat sich nichts gebrochen, sie hat sich nur verletzt.
7. Wir haben uns nicht wohl gefühlt, denn wir haben uns den Knöchel verstaucht.
8. Er wäscht sich jeden Tag, aber heute hat er sich auch die Haare gewaschen.
9. Hast du dich nur verletzt, oder hast du dir etwas gebrochen?

B. 1. **mich**
2. dir
3. mich
4. mir
5. sich
6. sich
7. dich
8. mir
9. sich
10. euch

C. 1. **Ich habe mich verletzt.**
2. **Ich habe mir das Bein verletzt.**
3. Sie hat sich gekämmt.
4. Sie hat sich die Haare gekämmt.
5. Wir haben uns gewaschen.
6. Wir haben uns die Hände gewaschen.
7. Hast du dich verletzt?
8. Hast du dir den Fuß verletzt?

D. Answers will vary. Possible answer: When a sentence with a reflexive verb has a direct object, the reflexive pronoun must be in the dative case. Ich habe mir das Bein verletzt.

DATIVE CASE INSTEAD OF FÜR + ACCUSATIVE p. 93

A.

	Accusative	Dative
1. mich	✓	✓
2. mir		
3. mich	✓	✓
4. mir		✓
5. mir		
6. mich	✓	✓
7. mir		
8. mich	✓	✓
9. mir		

B. 1. **dir**
2. Ihnen
3. euch
4. dir
5. dir
6. dir
7. dir

C. 1. **Dieser Anzug ist mir viel zu teuer.**
2. Das Rad ist meiner Schwester zu klein.
3. Die Sonnencreme ist ihm zu teuer.
4. Das Wasser ist ihr zu kalt.
5. Die Pause ist uns viel zu kurz.
6. Das Wetter ist meinem Freund zu schlecht.
7. Die Erkältung dauert mir zu lange.
8. Der Pulli ist meinem Opa nicht warm genug.

D. 1. **Das Hemd ist mir zu groß.**
2. Die Bluse ist ihr zu teuer.
3. Der Gürtel ist ihm zu kurz.
4. Der Kaffee ist ihr zu süß.
5. Das Wasser ist uns zu kalt.
6. Die Creme ist ihnen zu fett.

7. Dan, das Wetter ist dir zu schlecht!
8. Herr K., die Suppe ist Ihnen zu heiß!

E. Answers will vary. Possible answer: A **für** + accusative construction can often be replaced with the dative case: Das ist zu teuer für mich. or Das ist mir zu teuer.

D. 1. **größer als**
2. so groß wie
3. so gut wie
4. gesünder als
5. so alt wie
6. älter als
7. jünger als
8. so jung wie

E. Answers will vary. Possible answer: The comparative form adds **-er**, the superlative form **-st**, or **-est**. Adjectives of one syllable add an umlaut to the vowel when a comparative or superlative ending is added.

KAPITEL 7

COMPARISON p. 95

A.

	Comparative	Superlative
1. My sister is older than Anna's sister.	✓	
2. She must be the oldest in the family.		✓
3. Who is the tallest in your family?		✓
4. Jack is. But I am taller than Brent.	✓	
5. Do you see better in these glasses?	✓	
6. I see the best in my contacts.		✓

B.

	Pos.	Comp.	Sup.
1. Unsere Wohnung ist größer als Opas.		✓	
2. Ja, das ist eine große Wohnung.	✓		
3. Wir haben die größte Wohnung im Haus.			✓
4. Diese Medizin ist besser als diese da.		✓	
5. Du, das ist aber auch eine gute Medizin.	✓		
6. Ich glaube, das ist die beste Medizin.			✓
7. Diese Umgebung ist viel schöner.		✓	
8. Wir haben auch eine schöne Umgebung.	✓		

C. 1. **billiger**
2. besser
3. lieber
4. mehr
5. schöner
6. größer
7. jünger
8. älter

ADJECTIVES p. 97

A. 1. We live in a little village in the beautiful Alps.
2. We have a small house with a large garden.
3. The garden has many trees and gorgeous flowers in the spring.
4. We also have a modern pool and a large grill in our backyard.
5. Grandma enjoys the old-fashioned kitchen and the cozy living room.
6. I have a large bedroom with a sunny terrace. It is beautiful!

B. 1. Wir wohnen in einem kleinen Dorf in den schönen Alpen.
2. Wir haben ein schönes Haus mit einem großen Garten.
3. Im Garten stehen alte Bäume, und im Frühling haben wir wunderschöne Blumen.
4. Wir haben auch einen ganz modernen Pool und einen großen Grill im Garten.
5. Oma hat eine altmodische Küche und ein gemütliches Wohnzimmer.
6. Ich habe ein großes Schlafzimmer und eine sonnige Terrasse.

C.

	Masculine	Feminine	Neuter
1.		✓	
2.	✓		
3.		✓	
4.	✓		
5.		✓	
6.	✓		
7.	✓		
8.			✓
9.		✓	
10.	✓		

11. ______ ______ ✓
12. ______ ✓ ______

D. Answers will vary. Possible answer: Adjectives that precede nouns have endings. The ending depends on the gender of the noun.

ADJECTIVE ENDINGS FOLLOWING EIN-WORDS *p. 99*

A. 1. **es / en**
2. es / e / en
3. e / es
4. es / en
5. en / e
6. en / en
7. es / er
8. es / en
9. en / e
10. en / en
11. en / es
12. es / en

B. 1. **neue**
2. gemütlicher
3. eigenes
4. großes
5. kühler
6. kleiner
7. ruhige
8. neuer
9. friedliches
10. saubere
11. sicheres
12. eigenes

C. 1. **einen grünen**
2. mein rotes
3. Ihr weißes
4. unser brauner
5. seinem alten
6. deine nette
7. eurem neuen
8. kein guter
9. einen spannenden
10. zwei tolle

D. Answers will vary. Possible answer: Adjective endings depend on the gender, number, and case of the nouns they modify.

KAPITEL 8

ADJECTIVE ENDINGS FOLLOWING DER AND DIESER-WORDS *p. 101*

A. 1. **e / en**
2. en / en
3. en / e
4. e / e
5. e / en
6. e / e
7. en / en
8. e / en
9. e / e
10. en / en
11. e / e
12. e / e

B. 1. **das blaue**
2. diesen grünen
3. Dieses bunte
4. diesen schicken
5. dieser weißen
6. Welche gelben
7. welcher kleinen
8. die olivgrüne
9. den türkisblauen
10. diese braunen
11. diesen alten
12. den schwarzen

C. Answers will vary. Possible answer: Adjective endings following **der** and **dieser**-words are different from adjective endings following **ein**-words.

KAPITEL 9

PREPOSITIONS *p. 103*

A. 1. We are driving to Munich, and we will stay in this city for three weeks.
2. I want to go on a boat ride down the Isar.
3. We might also go hiking in the mountains near Salzburg.
4. If the weather is bad, we could visit the cathedral instead of the mountains.
5. According to the guidebook, the pass is closed in the winter months.
6. The weather in Munich is warm in the summer, even after dark.
7. Among other things, we will eat at the Hofbräuhaus for a taste of the local cuisine.

Answers

B. 1. Die Kinder spielen mit ihren Bällen auf dem Schulhof.
2. Hinter dem Haus steht das Fahrrad von meinem Bruder.
3. Diese Platte aus den 70er Jahren ist für meine Großmutter.
4. Ein Schüler geht in das Klassenzimmer und schreibt „Ruhe!" an die Tafel.
5. In diesem Dorf gibt es eine Kirche aus dem 15. Jahrhundert.
6. Wenn du durch das Stadttor gehst, kommst du in die alte Innenstadt.
7. Unser Auto steht auf dem Parkplatz in der Fräuleinstraße.
8. Ich warte vor dem eleganten Café neben dem alten Rathaus.
9. Wir fahren nach Garmisch und von dort aus steigen wir auf die Zugspitze.
10. Ich war mit meinen Freunden eine Woche in den Bergen.

C.

	LOCATION	DIRECTION
1.	✓	
2.		✓
3.	✓	
4.	✓	
5.		✓
6.		✓
7.	✓	
8.		✓
9.	✓	

D. Answers will vary. Possible answer: The two-way prepositions **an, auf, in, hinter, vor, über, unter, neben,** and **zwischen** are followed by the dative case forms to indicate location, by accusative forms to indicate direction.

DATIVE PREPOSITIONS *p. 105*

A. 1. Fährst du heute mit dem Rad zur Schule?
2. Ich war zuerst beim Metzger, und jetzt gehe ich zum Bäcker.
3. Nach dem Kino gehe ich mit meinen Freunden ein Eis essen.
4. Dieses T-Shirt ist von meiner Oma und dieses Stirnband von meinem Opa.
5. Seit der Pause habe ich mit meinem Mathelehrer gesprochen.
6. Der Rolf kommt eben aus dem Buchladen neben der Schule.
7. Bei uns gibt es heute einen Kuchen von meiner Tante.
8. Nach der Fete kommen meine Freunde zu mir.
9. Wann gehst du denn mit mir zur Post?
10. Ich warte bei der Schule gegenüber der Post.
11. Seit meinem vierzehnten Geburtstag gehe ich einmal im Jahr zum Arzt.
12. Zu welcher Zeit kannst du mit deinen Geschwistern zu uns kommen?

B. 1. **mit / nach**
2. nach / zu
3. von
4. seit
5. gegenüber
6. neben
7. aus
8. nach
9. nach / mit
10. bei / mit

C. 1. **dem**
2. der / dem
3. der / den
4. der
5. dem
6. dem / der
7. dem

D. 1. **meinen / meinen**
2. unserem / unserer
3. deinem / deiner
4. ihrer / ihrem
5. seinen / seinem
6. unserem / unserem
7. unserem / unserer

E. Answers will vary. Possible answer: The prepositions **aus, bei, mit, nach, von, zu, seit,** and **gegenüber** are always followed by dative case forms.

ACCUSATIVE PREPOSITIONS *p. 107*

A. 1. **für**
2. um
3. durch
4. ohne
5. gegen
6. ohne
7. für
8. durch
9. ohne

B. 1. **meine / den**
2. meinen
3. meine / meinen
4. deinen
5. meinen
6. die
7. meinen
8. den
9. die

C. 1. **dem / den**
2. der / den
3. das / den
4. den / die
5. dem / der
6. den / durchs
7. den / den
8. zum / der
9. der / der
10. die / der
11. der / zum / der
12. dem / der

D. Answers will vary. Possible answer: The prepositions **durch, für, gegen, ohne, um** are always followed by accusative case forms.

KAPITEL 10

PREPOSITIONS USED WITH VERBS AND ADJECTIVES *p. 109*

A. 1. **für**
2. für *or* an
3. gegen
4. auf
5. über
6. auf
7. auf
8. mit

B. 1. **deine**
2. ihren
3. seinen
4. unseren
5. meine
6. deiner
7. ihren
8. deine

C. 1. **Ich habe kein Interesse an seiner Kamera.**
2. Interessierst du dich für seine Kamera?
3. Sie ist allergisch gegen Obst.
4. Ich suche einen Hund.
5. Ich freue mich auf meine Ferien.
6. Wir warten auf den Bus.
7. Auf wen wartest du?
8. Er ist mit meiner Tante verheiratet.
9. Das Hemd passt gut zu deiner Hose.
10. Ich bin mit deinen Noten zufrieden.

D. Answers will vary. Possible answer: Prepositions can be used in fixed combinations with certain verbs and adjectives.

NOUN OBJECTS OF A PREPOSITION: DA-COMPOUNDS AND WO-COMPOUNDS *p. 111*

A. 1. **it**
2. it
3. them
4. her
5. them

B. 1. Wir sprechen über das Spiel. / darüber
2. Wir sprechen über unseren Präsidenten. / über ihn
3. Ich interessiere mich für Politik. / dafür
4. Ich spreche gern über diese Schauspielerin. / über sie
5. Freust du dich auf die Ferien? / darauf
6. Meine Großeltern kommen aus Deutschland. / auf sie

C.

	FORMAL	COLLOQUIAL
1.	✓	
2.		✓
3.		✓
4.	✓	
5.	✓	
6.		✓

D. 1. **Worüber**
2. worüber
3. Wofür
4. Für was
5. auf was
6. worüber / worauf
7. Über was
8. Worüber

Answers

E. Answers will vary. Possible answer: Pronouns can replace noun objects of a preposition only if they refer to a person. If they refer to things, you use a **da-**compound or a **wo-**compound (in questions).

■ FUTURE TENSE *p. 113*

A. 1. **I will read a book about Napoleon.**
2. We will go to the movies.
3. Will you see the Matterhorn?
4. They will be in Berlin over the weekend.
5. Mr. Lewis will have some papers for you.

B.

	Future Tense	Present Tense
1.		✓
2.	✓	
3.	✓	
4.		✓
5.		✓
6.	✓	

C. 1. **wirst**
2. werde
3. wird
4. werden
5. werdet
6. wird

D. 1. **Ich werde dieses Buch nicht lesen.**
2. Wirst du heute mit Anke ins Kino gehen?
3. Anke wird keine Zeit haben.
4. Wann werdet ihr denn nach Berlin fliegen?
5. Wir werden erst im April fliegen.

E. Answers will vary. Possible answer: The future tense is formed by using the helping verb **werden** + an infinitive.

KAPITEL 11

■ POLITE REQUESTS (WÜRDE-FORMS) *p. 115*

A. 1. **Would you take me out to the ball game?**
2. Would you give me the book?
3. Would you bring chips to the party?
4. Would you pass the salt?
5. Would you sew this button on for me?
6. Would you come to see the play?
7. Would you turn off the TV?
8. Would you clean your room today?

B. 1. **würde**
2. würdet
3. würden
4. würden
5. würde
6. würdest
7. würden
8. würdet

C. 1. **Ich würde gern einen Salat essen.**
2. Was würdest du gern essen, Thomas?
3. Mark würde gern ein Steak essen.
4. Herr Brown würde gern Fisch essen.
5. Was würden Sie gern essen, Frau Bea?
6. Wir würden gern Milch trinken.
7. Mia würde gern ins Kino gehen.
8. Würdest du gern schwimmen gehen, Al?
9. Ich würde gern Tennis spielen.

D. Answers will vary. Possible answer: In polite requests, würde-forms are used together with an infinitive.

■ UNPRECEDED ADJECTIVES *p. 117*

A.

	Preceded	Unpreceded
1.		✓
2.		✓
3.	✓	
4.	✓	
5.	✓	
6.		✓
7.		✓

B.

	Preceded	Unpreceded
1.		✓
2.	✓	
3.	✓	
4.		✓
5.	✓	
6.		✓
7.	✓	
8.	✓	
9.		✓

C. 1. **rote**
2. Rote
3. griechischer
4. Griechischer
5. polnische
6. Polnische
7. italienische
8. Italienisches
9. deutsche
10. Deutscher

11. kaltes
12. warme

D. Answers will vary. Possible answer: Unpreceded adjectives show the gender, case, and number of the noun they modify.

POLITE REQUESTS (HÄTTE-FORMS) p. 119

A. 1. **hättest**
2. hätte
3. hättet
4. hätten
5. hätte
6. hätte
7. hätte
8. hätte
9. hätten

B. 1. Was hätten Sie gern?
2. Ich hätte gern Bratkartoffeln.
3. Meine Mutter hätte gern einen grünen Salat.
4. Mark hätte gern einen Kaffee.
5. Sara and John, was hättet ihr gern?
6. Wir hätten gern ein Glas Wasser.
7. Wer hätte gern Milch?
8. Wir hätten lieber Orangensaft.
9. Die Kinder hätten gern Eis.

C. 1. hätte gern frisches Brot.
2. hätten gern frische Erdbeeren.
3. hätte gern kalten Saft.
4. hätte gern heißen Kaffee.
5. hätten gern süße Schokolade.
6. hätten gern ungarischen Wein.
7. hätte gern deutsches Bier.
8. hättest gern italienisches Obst
9. hätte gern griechischen Käse.

D. Answers will vary. Possible answer: The **hätte-**form can be used to make polite requests. The word **gern** is usually used with the **hätte-**form.

Komm mit! German 3

Answers

Answers

KAPITEL 1

THE CONVERSATIONAL PAST (REVIEW) *p. 123*

A. 1. **gekauft**
2. gelesen
3. anprobiert
4. besucht
5. gewaschen
6. eingeladen
7. gebraucht
8. gefunden
9. abgehoben
10. gegossen
11. eingekauft
12. vorgeschlagen
13. aufgeräumt
14. gehabt
15. gewesen
16. ferngesehen

B. 1. **hast / gelesen**
2. bin / gegangen
3. haben / gegessen
4. hat / bedient
5. habe / gekauft
6. hast / angezogen
7. hast / mitgenommen
8. habe / vergessen
9. seid / gekommen
10. bist / geblieben

C. 1. **Wen hast du besucht?**
2. Was habt ihr gehört?
3. Wo hast du geschlafen?
4. Wann sind die Kinder gegangen?
5. Wie lange seid ihr geblieben?
6. Was hat er fotografiert?
7. Was hat dir nicht gefallen?
8. Wen hast du eingeladen?
9. Wo hat er gearbeitet?
10. Wie viel hat das gekostet?
11. Worüber hast du dich gefreut?
12. Was hast du ihm geschrieben?

D. Answers will vary. Possible answer: The present perfect tense is used to refer to the past, especially in conversation. It is formed by using the present tense of either **haben** or **sein** and a past participle.

KAPITEL 2

ADJECTIVES (REVIEW) *p. 125*

A. 1. **en / en**
2. e / en
3. e / es
4. e / er
5. en / er
6. en / en
7. en / en
8. e / e

B. 1. **e / en**
2. e / en
3. en / e
4. en / e
5. en / e
6. e / en
7. en / es
8. er / en

C. 1. **es / e**
2. e / en
3. en / es / e
4. e / en
5. es / e
6. e / e
7. en / en
8. en / e

D. 1. **e**
2. er
3. e
4. e
5. en
6. en
7. en
8. en

E. Answers will vary. Possible answer: The adjective ending depends upon whether the adjective follows a **der** or **dieser**-word, or an **ein**-word. Unpreceded adjectives must show the noun gender.

KAPITEL 3

INFINITIVE PHRASES *p. 127*

A. 1. We are trying to think positively.
2. I am prepared to study hard.
3. We all must work harder. *none*
4. She's planning to fly to Europe this summer.
5. My cousins are ready to go to school in the fall.
6. Jacob plans to buy a new bicycle.
7. She should buy herself new clothes. *none*
8. What have you decided to do after class?

B. 1. **zu lernen.**
2. , heute Abend zu lernen.
3. zu gehen.
4. , ins Kino zu gehen.
5. abzunehmen.
6. , bis Ostern abzunehmen.
7. aufzupassen.
8. , heute aufzupassen.

C. 1. **um Geld zu sparen.**
2. um eine Reise zu machen.
3. um nicht zuzunehmen.
4. um mich abzulenken.
5. um etwas abzunehmen.
6. um mich zu waschen.
7. um mir die Haare zu waschen.
8. um mich modisch anzuziehen.

D. 1. **Ich versuche zu schlafen.**
2. Ich versuche, acht Stunden zu schlafen.
3. Ich habe vor zu lernen.
4. Ich habe vor, heute Abend Deutsch zu lernen.
5. Ich mache Sport, um fit zu bleiben.

E. Answers will vary. Possible answer: The word **zu** precedes the infinitive in infinitive phrases. In the case of verbs with a separable prefix, **zu** goes between the prefix and the infinitive. A comma is generally used when more words extend the infinitive phrase.

KAPITEL 4

ORDINAL NUMBERS *p. 129*

A. 1. I'm arriving on the fifteenth of June.
2. Our vacation begins on the third of April.
3. My birthday is on the seventh of January.
4. I am the second child of four.
5. Today is my parents' twentieth anniversary.
6. The twenty-second falls on a Monday.
7. She is making her third attempt to climb this wall.

B. 1. **siebten**
2. dritte
3. einunddreißigste
4. achten
5. vierzehnten
6. ersten
7. zweiten
8. achtzehnten
9. zweiten

C. 1. **fünfzehnten**
2. sechzehnten
3. ersten
4. drittes
5. ersten
6. vierten
7. vierzigsten
8. zweites
9. fünfzigsten

D. Answers will vary. Possible answer: Ordinal numbers add **-t** or **-st** to cardinal numbers. A few ordinal numbers are completely different from the cardinal number. When used as adjectives, ordinal numbers have adjective endings.

Answers

RELATIVE PRONOUNS AND RELATIVE CLAUSES *p. 131*

A. 1. Where does the friend who called you last night live?
2. Here is a book that I enjoyed reading.
3. Cookies that have raisins in them are my favorite.
4. Here comes the girl with whom I'm not speaking.
5. Over there is the math teacher I had last year.
6. He is buying the same computer that he used at his friend's house.

B. 1. **Mom went to the supermarket that is nearby.**
2. The girls who sing in the choir are coming along.
3. My friend Jacob, with whom I went to the movies last weekend, will be here soon.
4. I like clothes that are comfortable and inexpensive.
5. The guy who was injured on the trail is in the hospital.
6. We're talking about the math teacher who gives really hard tests.
7. The team that went to championship last year is even better this year.
8. There is the raccoon that always knocks over our trash cans.

C. 1. Ich habe Eltern, die ganz vernünftig und tolerant sind.
2. Mein Bruder, der drei Jahre älter ist, geht in die gleiche Schule.
3. Ich habe viele Freunde, mit denen ich mich gut verstehe.
4. Ich habe auch einen Freund, mit dem ich am Samstag ins Kino gehe.
5. Eine Lehrerin, mit der ich mich gut verstehe, trifft sich mit uns nach der Schule.
6. Ich bin auch in einer Clique, die sich immer am Freitag trifft.
7. Meine Freundin, mit der ich in den Ferien weg war, ist auch in der Clique.
8. Oft gehen wir in ein Café, das gleich in der Nähe ist.
9. Dort sprechen wir über ein Problem, das wir alle haben: viel Zeit und wenig Geld.

D. 1. **Die Clique, der ich angehöre, ist ziemlich groß.**
2. Mein Opa, der schon siebzig Jahre alt ist, kommt zu meiner Party.
3. Die Mädchen, die im Chor mitsingen, kommen auch.
4. Die Leute, mit denen ich ich ab und zu ausgehe, sind älter als ich.
5. Der Mathelehrer, über den wir gern reden, ist erst 30 Jahre alt.
6. Diese Schüler, die in diesem Café zusammenkommen, sind in meiner Klasse.
7. Dort kommt meine Freundin, mit der ich heute Abend ins Kino gehe.
8. Mein Opa, mit dem ich nach Milwaukee fliege, wohnt am Bodensee.
9. Meine Kusine, mit der ich an der Nordsee war, kommt uns besuchen.

E. 1. **die**
2. denen
3. der
4. den
5. dem
6. den
7. der
8. die
9. die
10. die

F. 1. **Der Film, den ich gestern Abend gesehen habe, war toll.**
2. Der Freund, den ich besucht habe, wohnt in Berlin.
3. Das Lied, das ich eben gehört habe, ist sehr populär.
4. Der Brief, den du geschrieben hast, ist zu lang.
5. Die E-Mail, die ich bekommen habe, ist von meiner Mutter.
6. Ich habe die Fotos, die du gemacht hat, sehr gern.

G. Answers will vary. Possible answer: Relative pronouns introduce relative clauses. The relative pronoun depends upon the gender and number of the antecedent and its own function in the relative clause (it can be a subject, direct or indirect object, or the object of a preposition, for example).

CONDITIONAL SENTENCES p. 135

A.
1. were / would
2. had / would
3. had / would
4. were / would
5. had / would
6. were / would

B.
1. würdest / hättest
2. hätte / würde
3. würdet / hättet
4. hätten / würden
5. würde / hätte
6. hätte / würde
7. würden / hätten
8. hätten / würden
9. würdet / hättet
10. hätten / würden

C.
1. Wenn ich Zeit hätte, würde ich mit dir an den Strand gehen.
2. Wenn Max Hunger hätte, würde er eine große Pizza essen.
3. Wenn wir Durst hätten, würden wir Wasser mit viel Eis trinken.
4. Wenn du Glück hättest, würdest du das Schachspiel gewinnen.
5. Wenn wir in München wären, würden wir zum Oktoberfest gehen.
6. Wenn ich in Berlin wäre, würde ich eine Bootsfahrt auf der Havel machen.
7. Wenn ihr in Hamburg wäret, würdet ihr in einem feinen Hotel übernachten.

D. Answers will vary. Possible answer: Conditional sentences consist of a wenn-clause and a würde-clause. In the wenn-clause, a form of hätte or wäre is used; in the würde-clause, a würde-form and an infinitive are used.

THE POSSESSIVE: GENITIVE CASE p. 137

A.
1. Do you know the color of the book?
2. Have you seen Jordan's math test?
3. The scent of a rose is wonderful.
4. Jack's house is on a river.
5. What is the name of the state flower of Texas?
6. She is dating the son of the mayor.

B.
1. meiner Eltern
2. des Opas
3. eines Freundes
4. meiner Freundin
5. deiner Freunde
6. dieser Stadt
7. unserer Hauptstadt
8. des Landes Bayern
9. ihrer Tochter

C.
1. meines Vaters
2. meiner Tante
3. meiner Kinder
4. seines Freundes
5. des Opas
6. der Großmutter
7. des Mädchens
8. der Stadt

D.
1. Das ist das Auto meines Vaters.
2. Wo ist das Haus deiner Tante?
3. Wo ist das Hotel deiner Eltern?
4. Wo ist die E-Mail deines Freundes?
5. Ich höre das Bellen ihres Hundes.
6. Hier sind die Bücher der Kinder.
7. Wo ist das Rad meines Onkels?

E. Answers will vary. Possible answer: In German, genitive case forms can be used to indicate possession. The genitive case of the definite article is des for masculine and neuter nouns, der for feminine and plural nouns. The genitive case for possessive adjectives is meines for masculine and neuter nouns, meiner for feminine and plural nouns. In addition, one-syllable masculine and neuter nouns add -es, or -s when they have more than one syllable.

Answers

KAPITEL 5

MODAL VERBS: PAST TENSE *p. 139*

A.

	PRESENT	PAST
1.		✓
2.	✓	
3.		✓
4.	✓	
5.	✓	
6.		✓
7.		✓

B.
1. **konntest**
2. musste
3. wolltet
4. konnte
5. mochtest
6. sollten
7. durfte
8. konnte
9. mussten

C.
1. **Ich konnte heute nicht zur Schule gehen.**
2. Ich musste zu Hause helfen.
3. Er konnte mich nicht anrufen.
4. Sie wollte eine E-Mail schicken.
5. Wir wollten nicht bleiben.
6. Ich sollte dir das sagen.
7. Musstest du allein zu Hause bleiben?

D. Answers will vary. Possible answer: In the past tense, modal verbs do not have an umlaut. The endings for the different persons are: **te, -test, -te, -ten, -tet, -ten**.

KAPITEL 6

NARRATIVE PAST (IMPERFECT) *p. 141*

A.
1. Who ~~watched~~ the movie last night?
2. We ~~played~~ soccer.
3. Who ~~said~~ we ~~came~~ back in the evening?
4. Who ~~heard~~ the news this morning?
5. They ~~saw~~ us as soon as we ~~left~~ the house.
6. I ~~bought~~ you an ice cream cone.

B.
1. **fuhr**
2. sah
3. kannte
4. trank
5. sprach
6. dachte
7. fragte
8. hörte
9. kam
10. aß
11. schlief
12. gab

B.
1. **verbrachten**
2. wohnten
3. aßen
4. fuhren
5. kauften
6. gefiel
7. fanden
8. lag / las
9. regnete / spielten

C. Answers will vary. Possible answer: The imperfect is used mainly in narration of longer sequences of events. Weak verbs add the past tense marker **-t** before the verb ending. Strong verbs do not have an ending in the first and third person singular. Strong verbs often have a vowel change.

SUPERLATIVE FORMS OF ADJECTIVES p. 143

A.

	Positive	Comparative	Superlative
1.		✓	
2.			✓
3.	✓		
4.	✓		
5.		✓	
6.			✓
7.			✓
8.		✓	

B. 1. **längste**
2. meiste
3. jüngste
4. kleinste
5. höchste
6. älteste
7. kürzeste
8. kälteste
9. besten
10. größte

C. 1. **kältesten**
2. höchsten
3. jüngste
4. ältesten
5. beste
6. längsten
7. meiste
8. härteste
9. wärmsten

D. 1. **am schönsten**
2. am besten
3. am kältesten
4. am längsten
5. am meisten
6. am liebsten

E. Answers will vary. Possible answer: The superlative form of adjectives adds **-st** to the positive form or **-est** when the positive form ends in **-d, -t, -sch,** or **-z.** In addition, many adjectives take an umlaut in the superlative form, as in the comparative form. When used before a noun, the superlative form takes adjective endings.

KAPITEL 7

RELATIVE CLAUSES (CONTINUED) p. 145

A. 1. **who**
2. that
3. which
4. that
5. that
6. where

B. 1. **was**
2. was
3. was
4. wo
5. was
6. was
7. was
8. wo

C. 1. **Das ist alles, was ich weiß.**
2. Es gibt viel, was du nicht weißt.
3. Das ist etwas, was ich gebrauchen kann.
4. Es gibt wenig, was ich brauche.
5. Ich schreibe nichts, was ich nicht sagen kann.
6. Du hast geschrieben, was ich toll finde!
7. Das ist alles, was ich gesagt habe.
8. Ich wiederhole alles, was ich höre.

D. Answers will vary. Possible answer: The word **was** is used to introduce relative clauses when **was** refers to the indefinite pronouns **das, alles, etwas, nichts, wenig,** and **viel.** The word **was** is also used to refer to the entire idea of the preceding clause.

KAPITEL 8

CONJUNCTIONS *p. 147*

A. 1. I said this to you because I was afraid I would hurt you.
2. I don't know what I said, but I know that I was right.
3. Dustin, you must wash your car before you take us to the concert.
4. You must wash the car, and then you must wax it, too.
5. I did not call you last night because I was angry at you.
6. Call me tonight, and I promise I will not hang up on you.

B. 1. Wir fliegen nach Florida, und wir mieten uns dort ein Auto.
2. Wir mieten uns ein Auto, wenn wir am Flughafen ankommen.
3. Wir haben ein Motelzimmer, damit wir uns erst einmal ausruhen können.
4. Am Strand ist es sehr schön, aber wir dürfen nur einen Tag dort bleiben.
5. Ich glaube aber, dass wir wieder einmal hierher kommen.
6. Als wir in Los Angeles waren, haben wir uns das Getty-Museum angesehen.
7. Es hat uns echt gefallen, weil das Museum viele gute Maler ausstellt.
8. Wir wollten noch einmal hinauffahren, aber wir hatten dann keine Zeit mehr.

C. 1. **Ich fliege nach Deutschland, weil ich Deutsch lernen möchte.**
2. Ich wohne bei einer deutschen Familie, damit ich die Gebräuche kennen lerne.
3. Meine Gastfamilie hat zwei Kinder, und die sind so in meinem Alter.
4. Ich höre die Deutsche Welle, damit ich auch ein bisschen über Politik weiß.
5. Ich nehme meinen Laptop mit, damit ich meinen Freunden E-Mails schicken kann.
6. So ein Laptop ist prima, weil ich dann drüben die Zeitung lesen kann.
7. Ich möchte dir eine E-Mail schicken, aber ich habe deine Adresse nicht mehr.
8. Schick mir deine E-Mail-Adresse, weil ich dir E-Mails schicken möchte.

D. Answers will vary. Possible answer: The coordinating conjunctions **und, oder, aber, denn** join coordinate clauses. The word order does not change. The subordinating conjunctions, such as **dass, als, wenn, weil, während, ob, damit,** join a main clause and a subordinate clause. The conjugated verb in the subordinate clause must be in last position.

KAPITEL 9

SUBJUNCTIVE FORMS OF MODALS *p. 149*

A. 1. **könntest**
2. könnten
3. könntet
4. könnten
5. könnte
6. könnte
7. könntest
8. könnte

B. 1. **wäre**
2. wärest
3. wäre
4. wären
5. wäret
6. wären
7. wäre

C. 1. **Ich wollte, ich könnte dir eine E-Mail schicken.**
2. Ich müsste zuerst einen Computer kaufen.
3. Aber du könntest mir eine E-Mail schicken.
4. Was könnte ich für dich tun?
5. Du könntest mir ein Handy kaufen.
6. Ein Handy sollte nicht mehr als 40 Euro kosten.
7. Ich wollte, ich wäre in den Bergen.

D. Answers will vary. Possible answer: The subjunctive forms of modals and **sein** can be used to express attitudes or wishes. The modals use the imperfect form with an umlaut (**ich könnte, müsste,** etc.), and **sein** uses the **wäre-** forms.

THE PASSIVE VOICE *p. 151*

A. 1. I didn't know that this magazine was read by so many people.
2. Beer and soft drink cans are being recycled in almost every community.
3. My picture is being taken tomorrow.
4. Did you know that my car is being worked on this afternoon?
5. This new film is being introduced today nationwide.
6. Do you remember where this movie was filmed?

B. 1. **wird / gezeigt**
2. wird / gemacht
3. werden / gesammelt
4. wird / gewählt
5. werden / gegossen
6. werden / eingeladen

C. 1. **wird das Licht ausgemacht**
2. werden Alu-Dosen wieder verwertet
3. wird der Müll zum Container gebracht
4. wird der Abfall weggeworfen
5. wird dein Auto gewaschen
6. werden die Läden heute geschlossen

D. 1. **werden / n / n / gelesen**
2. werden / n / n / getragen
3. wird / en / n / gespielt
4. wird / em / en / gegessen
5. wird / n / en / getrunken

E. Answers will vary. Possible answer: In the passive voice, the grammatical subject is the recipient of the action. A conjugated form of **werden** is used together with a past participle. If the performer of the action is known, it can be expressed by using **von** and the dative case.

CONDITIONAL SENTENCES (CONTINUED) *p. 153*

A. 1. **If I had had the patience, I would have sat through the performance.**
2. If we had had the money, we would have bought you a computer.
3. If our dad had broken his leg, he would have gone to Dr. Gutbein to have it fixed.
4. I would not have gone to school if I had had a cold as bad as yours.
5. Mother would not have cooked tonight if she had not bought a chicken.
6. If she had had plenty of groceries in the house, she would not have gone shopping.

B. 1. **hätte / würde**
2. hätte / würde
3. wäre / würde
4. wären / würden
5. wäre / würde

C. 1. **Wenn wir Hunger gehabt hätten, hätten wir etwas gegessen.**
2. Wenn ich schlauer gewesen wäre, hätte ich auch Chinesich gelernt.
3. Wenn ich mehr Zeit gehabt hätte, wäre ich an die Ostsee gefahren.
4. Wenn die Schüler hungrig gewesen wären, wären sie in einen Imbissladen gegangen.
5. Wenn du älter gewesen wärest, wärest du zur Bundeswehr gegangen.
6. Wenn Jonathan ein Auto gehabt hätte, wäre er mit uns an den Strand gefahren.

D. Answers will vary. Possible answer: The conditional can be used in "if ... then" statements. The **hätte-** and **wäre-**forms are used in the condition, and the **würde-**forms are used in the conclusion. Conditional sentences can also begin with the conclusion, followed by the condition.

KAPITEL 10

PASSIVE VOICE (SUMMARY) *p. 155*

A.
1. **wird / gefeiert**
2. werden / gezeigt
3. wird / gespielt
4. werden / verkauft
5. wird / aufgeführt
6. werden / begrüßt
7. wird / gegeben

B.
1. **Dieser Film ist nicht gezeigt worden.**
2. Das Stück ist nicht gespielt worden.
3. Die Halle ist heute repariert worden.
4. Ich bin nicht gefragt worden.
5. Wir sind nicht gefilmt worden.
6. Ich bin wieder fotografiert worden.
7. Kurt ist nicht abgeholt worden.

C.
1. **muss / gezeigt werden**
2. darf / gesehen werden
3. soll / gefilmt werden
4. will / gestört werden
5. können / gefunden haben
6. muss / verboten werden

D.
1. **Der Tisch muss repariert werden.**
2. Der Tisch soll repariert werden.
3. Der Tisch ist repariert worden.
4. Der Tisch wird repariert werden.
5. Hier wird nicht geraucht.
6. Hier wird nicht gesprochen.
7. Hier wird nicht getanzt.

E. Answers will vary. Possible answer: The passive is used in all tenses and with modal verbs. There is also an impersonal passive construction introduced by the word **es**; however, **es** can also be omitted.

KAPITEL 11

FUTURE PERFECT AND PERFECT INFINITIVE *p. 157*

A.
1. They will have received many gifts when the baby is born.
2. She will have finished the paper by the end of the semester.
3. Dad will have bought a new car by then.
4. I will have gone on vacation before Thanksgiving.
5. Katie will have visited the park often.

B.
1. Ich möchte wissen, wann du dein Studium beendet haben wirst.
2. Wir wollen hören, wenn sie ihr erstes Geld verdient haben wird.
3. Wenn ich um die Welt gereist sein werde, werde ich dir schreiben.
4. Sie kann schon ihren Schulabschluss gemacht haben, wenn sie 18 Jahre sein wird.
5. Wenn er 25 Jahre sein wird, muss er sein Studium abgeschlossen haben.
6. Wenn er aus den Staaten zurückkommen wird, wird er sehr viel gesehen haben.
7. Wir werden die Zeitung lesen und werden uns sehr gut informiert haben.

C.
1. **begonnen haben**
2. gekauft haben
3. gereist sein
4. geschrieben haben
5. angefangen haben
6. gehabt haben
7. gewesen sein

D. Answers will vary. Possible answer: The future perfect is used to express action completed at a specific time in the future. The future perfect consists of a present tense form of **werden** and the perfect infinitive, consisting of a past participle and the infinitive **haben** or **sein**.